GUIDE TO
PRINTED CIRCUITS

GUIDE TO
PRINTED CIRCUITS

by

GORDON J. KING
R.Tech.Eng., M.I.P.R.E., M.I.T.A.I., F.S.R.E.

FOUNTAIN PRESS:LONDON

Fountain Press Limited
46/47 Chancery Lane
London WC2A 1JU

First Published 1971

Printed in England by Offset-Litho at
Page Brothers (Norwich) Ltd.

CONTENTS

Soldering iron types. Bit efficiency. Efficient soldering. Heat shunts. Desoldering tools. Soldering precautions. Soldering guns. Desoldering braid. Desoldering heads. Temperature control. Servicing aspects. In-circuit testing. Breaks. Replacing components.

PREFACE

THIS IS NOT INTENDED to be a scientific dissertation on printed circuits. It was written essentially with the enthusiastic amateur, experimenter and the radio service apprentice and technician in mind, radio being used here in the broadest sense. I have endeavoured to trace the story of printed circuit boards, to show how they are designed and made in industry, how they can be made at home by the experimenter and enthusiast, how they are best repaired, the available substitutes, finalising with a chapter on the future, which is concerned basically with monolithic integrated circuits and thin-film configurations.

It has purposely been my intention to include substantial information on the recent printed circuit board substitutes since these are being used increasingly for educational purposes at schools, colleges and in the home as well as in the laboratory for speedy circuit 'mock-ups', as are the 'breadboarding' modules, which I have also considered in some detail.

I have paid special attention to the two most important printed circuit board servicing operations, namely soldering and desoldering, and have described some of the more recent soldering tools and equipment. Alas, it was obviously not possible to refer to the whole of the astonishingly wide range of such equipment which has been generated during the last three or four years; neither was it possible to mention the names of all the manufacturers who are currently producing and distributing soldering equipment, and I would wish to stress that lack of mention of any particular brand, name or range is in no way derogatory. The same is true of all the other items of equipment to which I have referred in this book.

Equipment, printed circuit boards, solid-state devices and instruments are continually being improved, with new models superseding the preceding ones. Thus, by the time this book appears in print there can be no guarantee that the items actually referred to or illustrated will be available; though there is every likelihood that a discontinued item, process or system would have been replaced by an improved equivalent.

For an up-to-date appraisal of the state of the art in the areas over which this book covers, the advertisement pages of magazines devoted to the enthusiast, such as *Practical Wireless, Television, Hi-Fi Sound, H-Fi News, Radio Constructor* and *Wireless World*, can be extremely useful.

In conclusion I wish to convey my sincere thanks to all those firms and individuals, too numerous to name separately, who have in some way or other assisted with the birth of this book and have thus helped to open the window upon a somewhat neglected aspect of electronics a little wider.

Gordon J. King   *Brixham, 1971*

CHAPTER ONE

INTRODUCTION

SINCE THE ADVENT OF THE ELECTRICAL CIRCUIT until about two decades ago, all electrical and electronic equipment was composed essentially of the appropriate components linked together by separate and free conductors for current conduction. This technique produces the so-called *wired circuit*. A *printed circuit* differs from this in that the system of electrical links—that is, the circuit—is 'printed' in copper on a special, high resistance laminate or 'board'. Holes are drilled in the board at the conductor link terminations to accept the leadout wires of the components. Thus the components are mounted usually on the plain side of the board and their wires soldered to the circuit complex on the 'printed' side. Some of the components, too, are sometimes formed on the laminate by a method of 'printing'.

Current Carriers

Any item of equipment in which electricity is utilised relies on low resistance conductors between the components to facilitate the movement of current carriers from one to the other in the manner intended by the designer. The original way in which this was achieved was by copper wires or large section copper or aluminium bars or strips, depending on the magnitude of circuit current.

All electronic equipment—such as radio and television receivers, audio amplifiers, hi-fi and telephone equipment and so forth—utilised fairly thin copper wires, insulated with rubber, cotton and/or enamel, and connected to the various components by screw terminals (an early idea) or soldered to special tags carried by the components for this sole purpose.

The circuits carrying somewhat heavier currents than the type of electronic equipment just mentioned—such as light industrial equipment, car wiring, domestic electrical wiring and so forth—are composed mostly of medium size copper conductors insulated with rubber, or a rubber compound or plastics to suit the environment in which they are used. These are bonded to the components by screw terminals or specially-shaped clamping washers and spring washers to keep the screw in low resistance contact with the wire.

Heavy power circuits—as found in power station transmission and distribution systems, for example—utilise large copper or aluminium (the latter for weight advantage) bars. These are rigidly clamped and bolted to the massive components and switchgear

As already implied, the printed circuit has superseded the wired circuit in all areas of electronics; it is also making itself felt in the design of higher current equipment, including light electrical switchgear, electric motors, control panels. Even motor cars are now adopting printed circuits for their electrical control panels! However, the circuit systems handling very large electric currents still employ the original schemes, and as yet there are no signs of significant changes in this area of circuitry.

Various factors led to the evolution of the printed circuit, and in the electronics world a major factor was the rising costs of labour in hand-wiring such things as portable radios, television sets and so forth. During the last twenty years the demand for this sort of equipment has risen at an astonishingly high rate, and the cost of mass production based on hand wiring, involving the selection of the appropriate coded wire, cutting to length, stripping, soldering and finally checking by a supervisor, greatly inhibited competition, especially with overseas markets.

Dry Joints

Further, in hand-wired circuit assemblies a so-called 'dry joint', resulting from bad soldering by unskilled labour, can instigate considerable trouble not only in the manufacturing area but also in the field, where its presence may be first observed by the owner of, say, a television set. This is, indeed, one of the major problems of dry joints—they have the habit of not revealing themselves until after the equipment has left the factory. It then becomes the job of the dealer's service technician to locate it—which is not usually a simple matter—and put it to rights.

I have known elusive dry joints to remain in equipment throughout its entire life period—defying all efforts of location—and producing very intermittent, though disconcerting symptoms of crackling, fading, variable picture definition and the like. It is not uncommon for the symptom to disappear for weeks on end when the equipment is shifted from its base environment to a dealer's workshop—and when it is not present it is virtually impossible to determine exactly where it occurs in the circuit complex.

In addition to dry joints, the interconnecting circuit wires can become weakened or, indeed, partially severed when the insulation is stripped from them by unskilled operators. Such things, especially where a coil or similar component is made of stranded wire, can impair the overall performance of an item of equipment, but even if there is no apparent shortcoming at the time of testing at the factory, the weakened wire could possibly fracture at a later date, when the equipment is in the field.

Matching Parameters

Hand-wired circuits also have the disadvantage of not being 100 per cent reproducible. This means that while the basic electrical parameters—of circuit-to-circuit and component-to-component conduction—might well be satisfied in all reproductions, the circuit parameters related to high-frequency currents and signals are far more difficult to match exactly when the hand wiring technique is employed.

The proximity of the conductors jointing the various signal-carrying components together has always been a point where difficulties could occur if precise alignment according to the design was not strictly followed. Undesirable interaction—or incorrect designed-for capacitance values—between adjacent circuits is likely to make the equipment unstable (either causing it to change completely from, say, an amplifier into an oscillator or severely modifying its response characteristics, especially in the cases of tuned amplifiers of very high frequency) or even unworkable.

With circuits of a 'critical' nature—such as those handling h.f., v.h.f. and u.h.f. signal currents and voltages—reproduction by hand-wiring involves the use of extra parts, such as clamps, circuit bridges, special insulators and the like, thereby increasing not only the cost of the finished equipment but also the burden on the testing personnel.

To cut the cost and time of a wired installation—whether in a motor car, house or factory or, indeed, within an item of equipment such as a motor starter—it is desirable as far as possible to reduce the number of wire ends that have to be stripped and the number of connectors that have to be supplied, fixed and tightened. The impetus behind the creation of a new scheme of circuit construction is thus obvious when all the above considerations are borne in mind.

Servicing

At this juncture it should be made clear that while printed circuits possess indisputable manufacturing and cost advantages, they do tend to complicate matters of a general servicing nature. Indeed, when printed circuit boards first started to appear in quantity in domestic electronic equipment service technicians strongly made it felt that they were not at all welcome. It is a relatively easy matter with a wired-circuit to trace from component to component—the components usually being mounted on tag boards and panels— as a means of following, say, the 'signal' through the complex and of finding the resistor, capacitor or other component responsible for the fault.

It is fairly easy, too, to change components in the wired-circuit, simply by cutting their leadout wires close to the mounting tags and soldering in the replacements. On the other hand, it is very easy to disturb a servicing operation by inadvertently shifting the interconnecting wires relative to each other, thereby increasing and/ or decreasing the capacitance between them.

As time went on, however, technicians became more and more used to the printed circuit and, characteristic of their type, soon discovered ways and means of solving the servicing problems. Manufacturers helped in various ways; component numbers, for instance, were printed on the component side of the boards, the service manuals contained almost full-scale (sometimes larger-scale) drawings of the circuit boards, showing the arrangement of the wiring, the component numbers and the positions of the components on the boards and details for removing and replacing the components.

The technician also discovered that by arranging certain types of printed circuit board of a receiver, for example, under repair so that the light from a bulb passed though it from the rear he was able easily to follow the circuit from component to component even

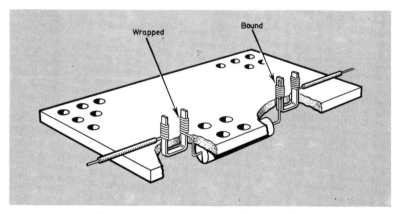

Fig. 1.1   Examples of "wrapped" connections.

without the manufacturer's printed circuit plan—for a comprehensive service manual is not always readily available! Such aspects of servicing printed circuit boards and equipment built around them are detailed in Chapter 5.

At the time of writing, the printed circuit board is almost exclusively employed in domestic electronic equipment. One maker was still building—and extensively advertising—television receivers based on the hand-wiring technique until a few years ago, but this has now been abandoned in favour of the printed circuit. The printed circuit system is here to stay; and while one or two isolated hand-wired products might continue for a while, the vast majority of products will be based upon printed circuits for some years yet to come. The printed circuit technique fits in admirably with the design of the type of equipment employing transistors, integrated circuits and other semiconductor devices.

Early Problems

When printed circuit boards first appeared on the domestic electronics horizon, most of the equipment built around them carried thermionic valves—including television sets and the small portable and semi-portable radio sets, as distinct from the slightly later miniature and sub-miniature transistored sets.

Valves and printed circuit boards do not make a particularly desirable partnership, especially when the valves are mains powered and run very hot, as in television sets. Special 'printed circuit type' valve holders were developed, but these failed to isolate adequately the heat of the valves from the printed circuit boards.

All was well when the equipment was fairly new, but after running for a year or so—sometimes less—the heat tended to scorch the boards and distort them mechanically. Depending on their nature of fixing to the main chassis matrix, high mechanical stresses were reflected into the laminate, and it was not an uncommon occurrence for the conductors to lift from the laminate, sometimes fracturing or shorting to adjacent conductors.

Moreover, convected heat from the valves attracted dust and dirt particles, and after several months use—especially in a smoky environment—a layer of scorched dust would appear in proximity to the hot valveholders! This had the effect of reducing the insulation resistance between the printed conductors, and played havoc in certain parts of the circuit. Television sets suffered badly, particularly in their field timebases, owing to h.t. conductors reflecting positive potentials, via the impaired or changing board insulation, to adjacent conductors associated with high impedance control grid circuits.

Symptoms stemming from this trouble included changes in field scan amplitude, progressive non-linearity at the top or bottom of the picture, hum bars across the screen and so forth. In many cases the trouble was never attributed to the printed circuit boards —not in the early days at least—and the unfortunate owners were often left with receivers needing constant adjustment to combat the effects of the changing insulation characteristics between the conductors.

Eventually, it was realised by service men that a high percentage of symptoms like this that could not be traced conclusively to a faulty component or valve was caused by printed circuit board idiosyncrasies—small wonder, then, that technicians were discouraged by this mode of design! In many cases a complete cure was possibly only by deleting the defective section of the printed circuit board and replacing it by more conventional wiring.

Base Laminates

Of course, when anything is new and under active development there are bound to be unforeseen problems, and it was not very long afterwards that those just mentioned were almost completely resolved. New base laminates were evolved with better insulating and temperature characteristics, and circuit designers became more criti-

Fig. 1.2   Inside view of tuner-amplifier using a printed circuit.

cal with regard to conductor placement, ensuring that those carrying h.t. potentials were as far as possible away from those associated with circuits of greater sensitivity—such as high impedance grid circuits.

The advent of the transistor gave printed circuit boards a renewed boost. In fact, without this mode of circuit construction the very small radios that we take for granted today would barely have been a feasible proposition. Transistors afterwards appeared in television sets—first the so-called hybrid models (being partly transistored and partly valved), followed by the all-transistor models, starting with the British Radio Corporation's all-transistor colour chassis, noteworthy here since it not only represented the first all-transistor colour set in the world, but because it also contains printed circuit boards or 'modules' which plug into the main chassis assembly, thereby facilitating the servicing of this sort of complex electronic equipment—and later in such equipment as r.f. and a.f. amplifiers, radio tuners, instruments and hi-fi 'building bricks'. The passing of the thermionic valve signified a new era in electronics—one in which the printed circuit in some guise or other, in partnership with the semiconductor, plays a predominate part.

Solderless Connections

At this stage, however, it should be mentioned that prior to the complete acceptance of the printed circuit scheme and its method of connecting components, another form of circuit connection was evolved which had the advantage of not requiring soldering, thereby improving reliability and to some extent reducing manufacturing costs. In this the two parts of the circuit are 'linked' by being clamped together with a tinned copper wire helix, placed in position by means of a special, powered 'wire twisting tool'.

The arrangement is such that the copper wire makes tight and very intimate connection with the edges of the special tabs used in the scheme. This is called a 'solderless' or 'wrapped' connection, and is illustrated in Fig. 1.1. The scheme is still used in some industries. While printed circuits are often terminated to external feed and take-off conductors by means of 'end connections' of the plug and socket variety, the solderless connection is also employed. Indeed, it is particularly appropriate with printed circuits where connection tabs have been established around the board.

Owing to the impact of the transistor radio, the portable television set, audio and hi-fi, it might be thought that the majority of printed circuit applications are confined to this field. This is not the case, since industry generally—taking in the telecommunications side—

is currently employing a higher proportion of all the printed circuits manufactured in any industrialised country than the proportion applicable to 'entertainment' equipment alone!

In the wide field of domestic electronics it is difficult to think of any item of equipment in which printed circuits are not used. Indeed, it might be said that the whole of the world-wide burgeoning of the 'entertainment' side of the electronics industry—concerned essentially with radio and television reception and disc and tape recording and reproduction—and, in more recent years, with many varieties of 'electronic toys', is in no small measure due to the advent of the printed circuit.

Contemporary Equipment

Let us now consider some examples of modern equipment. Fig. 1.2 depicts the printed circuit 'heart' of a modern tuner-amplifier, while Fig. 1.3, for dramatic comparison, shows a section of a similar item of equipment, but this time adopting the hand-wired technique!

It has been intimated that one of the problems associated with the servicing of printed circuit boards lies in the extraction of suspect components for substitution—a common servicing artifice with hand-wired equipment. Indeed, with hand-wired equipment this kind of exercise was not at all difficult, and very little effort was

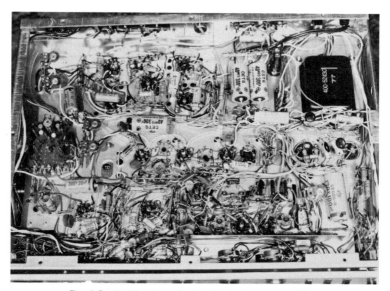

Fig. 1.3   Inside view of a hand-wired tuner-amplifier.

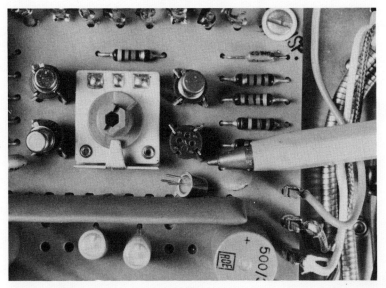

Fig. 1.4 Group of four plug-in transistors on a printed circuit board, showing one transistor removed from its special holder.

needed to replace a valve, but when it comes to substituting transistors in printed circuit boards the operation is wide open to hazards, and significant damage can result when the technician's skills fail to reach those necessary for printed circuit work (see Chapter 5).

However, even this by-product problem is being alleviated by the development of transistors with wire 'pins' and holders to match them. Fig. 1.4 shows a group of such transistors—with one removed from its holder—mounted in a hi-fi tuner-amplifier of American design. The British Mullard company, too, has developed a range of printed circuit board transistors devoid of the conventional leadout wires. These *Lock-Fit* transistors, avoid the need to follow the usual, often awkward, processes of fitting wire-ended transistors to new equipment. They also make it a little easier to extract already-fitted devices from circuit boards.

The usual procedure of transistor fitting amounts to pushing the three or four leadouts wires through the correct holes on the plain side of the printed circuit board, cutting them to length at the circuit side of the board, holding them in position and hoping they will hold steady while being soldered. Simultaneous fiddling with heat shunts between the device and the circuit to prevent excessive heat from being conducted to the transistor junctions through the leadout wires further complicates the operation.

The *Lock-Fit* transistors have specially-shaped connectors fitted to them. These are made of a tough metal, not easily bent or broken, and their design is such that they fit straight into the holes of standard printed circuit board grids, after which they can be easily soldered to the circuit conductors, This type of printed circuit board transistor is shown in Fig. 1.5.

For all those applications in the mass consumer markets, the most economically derived printed circuit is naturally sought, and may take the form of a board composed of synthetic-resin-bonded-paper (SRBP)—see Chapter 2—equipped with one-ounce copper foil (for the conductors)—sometimes on both sides of the board, depending on the application—with the utmost degree of automation being applied to hole drilling, cutting and component mounting.

In the earlier days the designer was sometimes handicapped because ordinary SRBP boards were not particularly suitable for the higher signal frequencies in the MHz ranges, and a synthetic-resin-bonded-fibre board (SBRF) or ceramic printed component parts had to be employed; but now, with the gradual but steady improvement in materials, it is possible in all but a few cases to adopt SRBP boards for almost every part of a mass-produced item of equipment.

The newest telephone instruments in Great Britain and other countries all incorporate printed circuit boards (see Fig. 1.6), while in the new solid-state telephone exchanges a multiplicity of computer-based, printed circuit boards are featured. For more specialised, industrial electronic equipment the SRBF board is more widely used, since the specification may call for a very high degree of resistance to mechanical vibration, corrosion, humidity and the like, while the dielectric losses at very high frequencies might well have to be diminished below that possible with the less exacting SRBP construction.

Strip Wave-guide

A fairly recent application of the printed circuit lies in the strip wave-guide or transmission line. Microwave signals—such as those used in radar, space communication, military activities and, to an increasing extent, tele-communications links—are often propagated either through coaxial cables or tubular wave-guides. Wave-guides consist of a polished metallic tubing (sometimes called 'trunking'), the sections of which are very accurately fitted together and matched. Coaxial cable also consists of a metal tube, but often flexible, as in television downlead, within which a central conductor is supported on insulators.

Fig. 1.5   Example of the Mullard *Lock-Fit* transistor system.

Fig. 1.6   The printed circuit insert of the Post Office telephones.

These metallic constructions are costly, and it has been possible to provide a workable alternative—known variously as *Microstrip* or *Tristrip*, depending on the maker—in which the printed circuit technique is adopted. In one example a flat strip of conductor is printed on one side of a long strip of 'dielectric' material, which carries a continuous copper foil over the whole of its reverse side.

This printed strip is covered with another strip of dielectric material that carries a foil on its upper side. The printed conductor is thus enclosed between two foil surfaces, separated by the dielectric—and it is called a *strip transmission line.*

Scan Coils

Flexible printed circuit strips, using a plastics film as the base, are also used to interconnect a system of printed circuit board sub-assemblies, and it is noteworthy that scanning coils for television sets are now being made along similar lines. The basic material consists of a sheet of good quality insulating material (*Mylar*, for example) of about 0·001in. (25μm) thick. This is coated on both sides with copper of between 0·0015–0·005in. (37–127μm) thick, according to the exact application. The pattern of conductors, eventually constituting the coils, is formed by etching away unwanted copper—in the same way that printed circuit boards are made (Chapter 2)—the pattern being derived from a master transparency prepared photographically. Thus, any number of identical sets of coil windings may be created from the single master.

Such coils have the advantage of very good geometrical accuracy —governed by the accuracy of the original 'master' as distinct from the skill of the assembler—excellent angular positioning of the vertical and horizontal axes (permitting tolerances within 0·2 deg.), small variations from coil to coil, ideal for matching sets for colour television cameras, for example, and compactness of assembly.

Both electrical and electronic measuring instruments, in which the range is changed by switching, employ printed circuit boards as a matter of course. These provide very accurate positioning contact areas and significantly minimise the possibility of inaccuracy through trouble with soldered joints. More sophisticated electronic instruments adopt printed circuit boards and plug-in modules for their electronics circuitry. A good example of this practice is given in Fig. 1.7, where at (a) shows the overall view of the inside of a colour television signal generator (Körting), using plug-in printed circuit board modules; (b) a 'close-up' of several of the modules *in situ*, and (c) and (d) respectively the printed circuit side and the plain (component) side of one module.

Non-electronic Applications

Printed circuits are also used in devices that are not primary 'electronic' in application. For example, many modern cameras

Fig. 1.7 Colour television pattern generator using printed circuit modules: (a)—above—overall view of the complete instrument. (b)—below—section view of the plug-in modules *in situ*. See also Figs 1.7(c) and (d).

feature 'magic-eye' devices whereby the output of a 'light cell' is used to work the opening of the iris in accordance with the available light. The whole of the switching and interconnecting arrangements for equipment like this must be accommodated within the smallest area, sometimes no larger than the inside of the lens mount proper. Soldered connections, of course, would be virtually impossible to process in such small dimensions, so a small printed circuit board— possibly no larger than a one new penny piece—makes up the switch, with suitably-plated contact surfaces, along with all the connections.

Modern electronic watches, which use timing oscillators and small mercury cells for power, incorporate connections and components which could not be handled other than by printed circuits. These are specially designed on a very thin backing, so diminutive that a watchmaker's glass is needed to distinguish the details.

In another field, a form of printed circuit finds application in the heating of glass. A glass of special heat-resistant quality is coated with a very thin layer of metal that has a high electrical resistance per unit volume. Paths are etched away from this, leaving a zig-zag resistance element. This is so proportioned that when a particular potential is applied across it the power dissipated produces the designed-for heating effect.

Strain Gauges

In many fields of engineering so-called 'strain gauges' are employed. In their simplest form, these comprise a short length of resistance wire secured to a flexible, plastics backing. This is arranged to adhere firmly to, say, a beam under stress or to the wing of an aircraft in flight. The wire—commonly copper-nickel alloy—varies in resistance as the strain on the test item varies. For instance, if the strain gauge is coupled to the wing of an aircraft, any deflection of the wing will change the wire tension, thereby changing its resistance, and this is detected by a suitable readout device.

The strain gauge, of which there is a legion of types, can be printed on a thin stock and coated with epoxy resin varnish. A multiplicity of such gauges might be coupled to a particular experimental project—the prototypes of a nuclear power station, for instance—and each one will give a particular readout, in terms of strain and stress, either on a conventional meter, digital counter or graph paper in ink from a pen recorder.

Greater Current Requirements

For power applications the resistance of the conductor must be as low as possible to avoid excessive heating, and where the con-

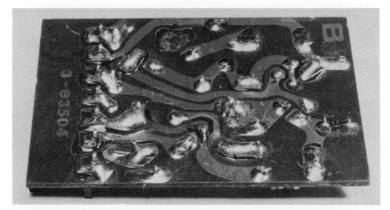

Fig. 1.7(c)—above—printed circuit side of one module of the pattern generator of Fig. 1.7(a), and the plain side of the module (d)—below.

ductor is a flat, copper strip the resistance can be lowered either by making it wider or thicker (or both). Thickening a printed circuit conductor is possible, but only by the use of a thicker copper foil for the entire circuit. In practice, instead of the widely used 1-oz. per sq. ft. (about 28 grams per 30 sq. cm.) copper foil (see Chapter 2), foil of up to 3-oz. (85 grams) copper [0·0045 in. (about 110μm) thick] may be used. Thickness dimensions in excess of this give rise to difficulties concerning the bonding of the conductor to the base material.

However, if this thickness of copper is still insufficient to allow a particular circuit to carry the required current without overheating, the only alternative is to redesign the circuit to make the affected conductors wider. In practice, attention is paid to the problems associated with the rise in temperature of the conductors relative to the circuit as a whole, considering also the associated components, plugs, sockets and so forth. The circuit, too, can bend or twist as the temperature rises, and this can impair the conduction or vary the resistance between, say, the board conductors and the outlet sockets—a very disconcerting effect, especially when the board is in the control panel of a motor car I know, having experienced this trouble!

A number of examples of such boards are already in service. Several car makers are using printed circuits—sometimes on a flexible, plastics, heat-resistant base material—to achieve all the complex connections that lie behind the facia board, linking the ignition switch, the water temperature gauge, the fuel gauge and all the other electrical equipment that centres on the dashboard (see Fig. 1.8). Printed circuits like this are sometimes also made on an SRBP base laminate, with the conductors in 3-oz. (85 gram) copper foil. This handles up to 30 amperes of current without appreciable temperature rise.

House Wiring

Printed circuits are also finding their way into some aspects of house wiring, one illustration being the printed circuit inserts used in connection boxes, these reducing wiring time since all the crossover connections required are already provided.

There is also a move towards the production of printed circuit commutators for small electric motors. In this application, the com-

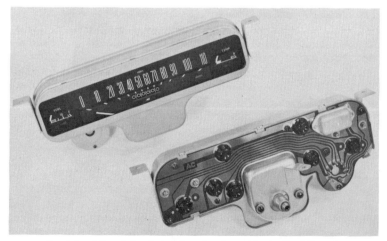

Fig. 1.8   Printed circuit dashboard unit used in the Ford *Corsair*.

mutator is built upon a suitable plastics base coated with a skin of copper, and the gaps needed between the segments are etched away in the manner of printed circuit production (see Chapter 2).

The multiplicity of electrical connections found behind the panels of the industrial electric motor starter and controls can nowadays be replaced by printed circuit boards. Thus, the electrician-fitter simply has to engineer the mains source to the appropriate terminals —all the other actions, previously necessary with hand-wiring, having been accommodated by the printed wiring.

The next few years are likely to see the advent of hundreds of applications of relatively small printed circuits for 'power'—as distinct from electronic—purposes, and one illustration is the confusion of electrical connections that reside behind the control panel of an electric cooker, involved with automatic switching devices and the variable controls for the hotplates, which could be handled more conveniently by printed circuits.

Cost Factor

To sum up, there is little in the nature of interconnections, switching and so forth to which the printed circuit principle cannot be applied; but manufacturers are naturally concerned with cost. The price of a printed circuit has to be compared with the cost of the manual work needed to make the connections by other methods, and particularly with the cost of making-off the final connections from the wiring complex, which could be a printed circuit, to the rest of the equipment. If soldering, wrapping or crimping is necessary for this operation, then it is possible that the cost of the printed circuit would not be justified, as soldering skill and wiring-jig equipment would be required anyway!

Printed circuits greatly favour mass-produced consumer markets, and for a few specialised items of equipment and prototypes the *Veroboard* (see Chapter 4) method of circuit fabrication represents another, possibly more desirable, method. In all aspects, however, the printed circuit technique has brought in its wake the demand for more suitable components, and in the field of electronics these include such components as volume controls, transistor holders, special coil and inductor mountings and, indeed, almost any discrete component that one can think of. Closely related to the printed circuit is the integrated circuit, and complete circuit assemblies, including resistors, capacitors as well as active semiconductor elements like transistors, are combined in a single small encapsulation little larger than a transistor; Chapter 6 has more to say about the integrated circuit.

CHAPTER TWO

DESIGN AND MANUFACTURE

A PRINTED CIRCUIT BOARD can be defined as an insulating base material to which is permanently attached a flat, metallic network of conducting paths whose dimensions are related to the nature of the currents handled by them. The base material may be a resin-coated paper, fibre-glass, glass or even ceramic, and it may not necessarily be of the familiar 'flat board' configuration.

Some base materials are flexible to allow the formation of 'bridge couplings'; for instance, between components that are movable relative to one another. The flat board configuration, however, is the most widely used, and it may be of the nature of a single, 'mother board' into which smaller boards are plugged, by the use of specially designed 'connectors', which ensure adequate and permanent, low resistance couplings.

Board Design

The metallic network—or circuit—may be impressed on one or both sides of the board, and holes are drilled through both the board and the metal terminations of the circuit to cater for the leadout wires of the components, which are soldered into the network in accordance with the original circuit design. Now, before we study the methods of printed circuit construction, it will be instructive to look first at the design.

This is a very important process, for once a printed circuit has been made it is virtually impossible to alter it. Thus, when a device requiring the use of a printed circuit has been evolved, the designer must carry out all the necessary experimental work to ensure that the various components and conductors are situated for the least interaction.

The placement of the components has to be carefully considered

18

to avoid the normal working action of one reflecting an adverse characteristic into another one which is adjacently placed. A typical practical aspect of this is the normal temperature rise of one component—say, a resistor—affecting another, critical component, like a capacitor or semiconductor.

After performing a number of 'exercises in logic', based on the nature and type of circuit configuration that the design requires, the circuit designer will turn to trial layouts to avoid the crossing of conductor paths in the circuit—or, if crossovers are unavoidable, arranging the configuration so that 'jumper leads' or actual components can cater for them. A circuit board carrying copper on both sides can also help to solve the problem of crossovers, especially when the circuit design calls for a multiplicity of them.

The Master Diagram

The next stage lies in the preparation of a 'master diagram', which is commonly made larger than the finished circuit; often twice as large, since this makes working on it that much easier, especially when the circuit is complex. Photography eventually reduces the size of the diagram to that of the circuit.

Design requires the observance of a number of 'rules'. One rule is that the space between the conductors must be strictly controlled to avoid the possibility of electrical discharge or unwanted capacitance. The amount by which the master drawing is to be reduced in size is thus a critical design factor.

Another rule is that the conductors (once called 'land') must be wider in those parts of the circuit that handle large currents (possibly at 50 or 60Hz mains frequency), where it is measured in amperes rather than milliamperes. Such current must be handled without undue temperature rise of the conductors, and in this respect it is noteworthy that a conductor strip about 0·4mm wide will carry 1·25 amperes with a temperature rise of 40deg.C, while double the width will carry almost three times the current (3.5 amperes) with the same temperature rise. These figures are based on 1-oz. copper foil.

Another rule is that the minimum width of a copper strip should not generally be less than about 1·5mm. This is related to mechanical strength rather than electrical properties; and it also ensures that the strip remains securely bonded to the base material. Excepting factors of capacitance, inductance and inter-conductor discharge possibilities from high voltages, the clear space between lands should not be less than $\frac{1}{16}$in. (1·58mm). Further, the points where the holes for the component leadout wires occur must be exactly sited to suit the dimensions of the components and the distances between the lead-out wires so that the components 'sit' correctly on the finished board. The conductor is also enlarged at the points of the holes, as shown in Fig. 2.1.

One method sometimes adopted for the preparation of the master drawing is shown in Fig. 2.2., which is a special pen-type holder designed to dispense adhesive tape to represent the copper connecting lines. This method of design is further enhanced by adhesive patches in the shapes of bends, hole connections, etc., which are available to the designer. These allow him rapidly to develop a circuit design with the minimum of laborious drawing work.

The master diagram should also provide for the etching of large areas of copper that remain on the board as may, for example, be necessary for the provision of 'earth return' paths. The whole area is not removed, only strips of it, as shown in Fig. 2.3. The idea is to avoid the deformation of the board when heat is applied for soldering the component leadout wires to the copper, since a large area of unwanted copper—differing in coefficient of expansion from the board material—is likely to expand sufficiently to cause it to pull away from the laminate.

Module Arrangement

The current trend in overall equipment design is to divide the complete system into sections and then to develop each section—in terms of both electronic design and printed circuit design—separately. The contemporary colour television set is a typical example in this respect. Either separate printed circuit sections are utilised,

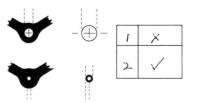

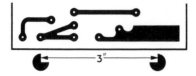

Fig. 2.1 Examples of the preparation of the master diagram.

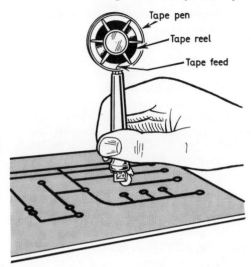

Fig. 2.2   Showing the application of a tape dispenser during the production of the master diagram.

Large areas of metal reduced by means of cross-hatching

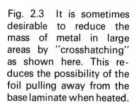

Fig. 2.3   It is sometimes desirable to reduce the mass of metal in large areas by "crosshatching" as shown here. This reduces the possibility of the foil pulling away from the base laminate when heated.

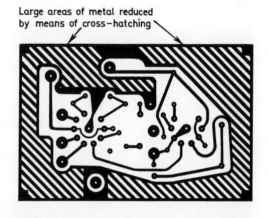

or a printed circuit 'module' scheme, whereby the mother board or, more commonly, a metal framework of some kind—is designed to cater for a multiplicity of plug-in boards. The inside of a colour television set adopting separate printed circuit sections, interlinked by cables, is shown in Fig. 2.4.

With the plug-in arrangement, each printed circuit board has all its connections brought to a row of strips along one edge, and these are designed to line-up with the 'sockets' of a female type connector, often termed an 'edge connector'. There is also an interlocking system so that a separate board can only be inserted the correct way round in its own particular connector. A selection of edge connectors from the ITT range is shown in Fig. 2.5.

Advantages of this idea are many-fold. For one thing, it assists the cabinet designer because the separate boards can be disposed at almost any convenient angle to suit his ideas. It also facilitates factory testing, since it is less difficult to locate faults on small subboards than on a large board containing all of the system's circuitry. A system composed of separate sub-boards is also easier and often less costly to service in the field, especially when the manufacturer supplies replacement sub-boards to the service agent or dealer. If a design modification is indicated after a system has been running in the field for some time, then this is far less costly to process when only a relatively simple sub-board is involved than when a single, large complex board caters for all the circuits and sections—there is less incentive to improve the design of a large board at that stage than a small sub-board.

Moreover, it may be economically justified to scrap a bad design, even at an advanced stage in its development, or a sub-board assembly in the field—along with all its components—should this

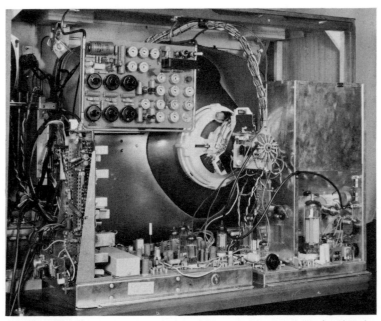

Fig. 2.4　The inside of a contemporary colour television receiver, showing the various interconnected printed circuit sections.

Fig. 2.5   Examples of edge connectors (STC).

be causing undue servicing trouble. In the latter connection, this could be less costly in the long run than endeavouring to clear an elusive fault that could account for a great deal of costly technician's time!

From the design aspect, a small sub-board is easier to handle than one large complex board; the master diagram, too, is obviously less detailed. This means that operators with lesser skills are generally able to handle the design work adequately, without expensive supervision, but under the watchful eye of the section controller.

Connection of Sub-boards

When the master diagrams are being prepared for sub-boards, though, due attention must be given to the manner in which they will ultimately be connected to the rest of the system and held in position on the matrix frame or mother board. Small boards may be sufficiently supported by being plugged straight into the mother board, which is, perhaps, being screwed down at all four corners.

Room must be allowed to yield adequate clearance on both sides of the board for the set screws, spring washers and other fixing hardware relative to 'live' metal fixings and components. A design shortcoming—as any service technician is eager to proclaim—is that printed circuit fixing demands the use of screws and screwdriver for which ample space has not been made available!

All of these factors have to be taken into account when the master diagram is being prepared. The diagram might also incorporate some sort of code, trade mark or sign, so that this will appear in copper print on the finished board. Such labelling is often used to identify a particular type of printed circuit.

It is important for the diagram to be drawn on the kind of paper, card or board that is proof against mechanical distortion due to humidity, temperature effects and so forth, since this could have the effect of altering the dimensions of the drawn lines, thereby reflecting similar errors into the finished circuit board. Bristol board or a special drafting card is a commonly used material for this kind of accurate work.

Making the P.C. Board

When the master diagram—probably twice the size of the real printed circuit board—has been evolved, the next major step consists of etching or dissolving the unwanted metal from the copper-clad board to create the circuit as depicted by the master diagram. It must be stressed that very accurate checking of the master is essential at this juncture, since alterations to the design become impossible once the etching has been put to hand.

It is now the task of the manufacturer of the equipment—or electronic device—to decide on how many printed circuit boards will constitute the initial run, and he will then either gear-up to make that quantity himself or contract the job out to a firm specialising in this particular field. Copper-clad laminate is available in standard sheets of about 2ft. square, although larger sheets can be ordered if required, assuming that the associated equipment—like cameras, etching baths and so on—will accommodate them.

Suppose that a customer orders a thousand boards of 8in. (20·3cm) by 12in. (30·5cm). The printed circuit board maker might then decide to multiply the drawing by six times, thereby developing a new master composed of the same layout in two rows of three. This might be done, for instance, to enable him to cover a 'standard' sheet of laminate with the six repeats in one go. There is no difficulty in separating them at a later stage to produce six identical, but separate boards.

The master print is mounted in a special frame on an easel facing a large camera, and with the aid of very powerful illumination the master diagram is clearly photographed on to a glass photo-sensitive plate—similar to that used in the early plate cameras. This is developed to give the photographic negative.

Next, a so-called 'step and repeat' camera is brought into operation. This comprises a camera body mounted so that it may be automatically moved an exact distance upwards, downwards or side-ways after each exposure. In this way, six (or whatever number is decided on) exact copies of the original master diagram are photo-graphed on to a single plate, and at this stage they are set out exactly to cover the 'standard' sheet of copper-clad laminate.

The Resist

The actual process of transferring the new, multiple master to the copper-clad laminate can be handled by several techniques, but

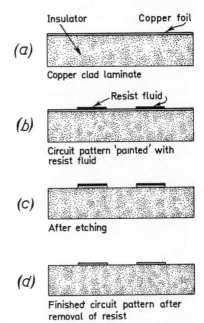

Fig. 2.6 Basic printed-circuit-making processes. The copper foil (a) is painted with resist fluid to retain the metal (b), as shown after etching (c). Finally, the re-sist and residual etching fluid are removed by washing (d).

(a)

Insulator   Copper foil

Copper clad laminate

(b)

Resist fluid

Circuit pattern 'painted' with resist fluid

(c)

After etching

(d)

Finished circuit pattern after removal of resist

before investigating these it is desirable to have in mind the ultimate aim of the process. The requirement, of course, is for a predeter-mined network of copper conductors, and these have to be derived from the continuous sheet of copper which backs the board. An acid etching fluid is employed to dissolve away the thin layer copper on the laminate except where it is required to provide the circuit conductors.

This obviously means that the copper surface must be coated very precisely with some kind of material which resists the etching fluid exactly where required, while failing to hinder the etching process elsewhere. The basic component in this process is called a *resist*, and it is specially developed to withstand the effects of the acid and to keep this away from the land that needs to be retained in accordance with the master diagram. The idea is revealed in Figs. 2.6 and 2.7.

We shall see in Chapter 3 that the amateur can make his own 'one-off' printed circuits without the bother of the photography just described; and, indeed, one-offs are often produced for prototype work—printed circuit 'do-it-yourself' kits being available for this purpose. The idea is to draw the circuit actually on to the copper surface of the laminate in resist—coloured to make the drawing show up clearly—and then to immerse the board so prepared into a bath of etching fluid so that all the copper, except that covered by the resist, is dissolved away. There is nothing to it, really!

There is another method more suitable for the production of relatively small numbers of boards in which a 'photosensitive' resist is adopted. Here a strong light is used to expose the photosensitive resist *through* the previously prepared negative, after which the copper-clad laminate is 'developed'—as in ordinary photography—in subdued light. It then emerges with the design of the original master printed upon it in an acid resisting chemical; with the remainder of the metal clean and clear, and ready for the etching process.

This sort of photosensitive resist is made in various ways by different manufacturers; but one type consists of a bichromated shellac to which is added chemicals that are light sensitive.

For mass production it is necessary to transfer the whole of the photographed detail from the large, glass negative 'plate' to the copper-clad laminates. Of the several schemes that have been evolved for this process, the two most widely adopted are (i) *offset lithography* and (ii) *silk-screen printing*.

The Offset Method

The offset lithographic method has been borrowed from the printing industry. Firstly, a zinc plate—called a *litho plate*—is evenly coated with a light sensitive emulsion possessing special characteristics. This is exposed from a powerful light passing *through* the negative plate (see Fig. 2.8) which, it will be recalled, is possibly showing a multiplicity of the original master diagrams. The exposed litho plate is then photographically developed so that the original art work is depicted in clear detail on its surface. The remainder of the plate is then covered with a hardened film of albumen.

Now, when an inked roller is passed over the litho plate, ink adheres only to the clear areas where the matt surface is untouched; it is repelled at the albumen-covered areas.

At this stage the lithographic offset principle comes into effect and the litho plate is fitted into a litho press. The basic principle involved is that the print on the litho plate is transferred to the copper surface of the laminate *via* a litho roller, contained within the press.

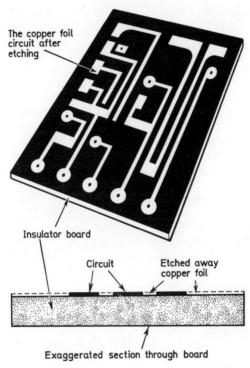

The copper foil circuit after etching

Insulator board

Circuit

Etched away copper foil

Exaggerated section through board

Fig. 2.7   Basic development of a printed circuit board.

The action is that an inked roller is caused to pass over the litho plate which, as we have seen, retains ink on the clear areas but repels it on the coated areas.

The next cycle of events is the traversing of the inked plate by the litho roller which, made of a special rubber, picks up the image of the plate, so to speak, on its surface. In other words, the image of the plate is offset on the litho roller, and from here it is transferred directly on to the surface of the copper. The litho press, of course, is designed to operate at high speed, thereby facilitating the mass production of printed circuit boards.

The 'ink' used for printed circuit work, of course, differs from that used for ordinary printing in that it is a *resist ink*, of which there is a whole range of patented varieties. The end result, therefore, is that the copper surfaces of the laminates have printed upon them in resist ink—making them ready for the etching process—the original drawing, possibly in multiples, as we have seen. Now, before we delve into the etching process let us run through the silk-screen printing idea.

The Silk-Screen Method

The prime element here, as would be expected, is a special kind of silk screen stretched over a frame of appropriate size. The silk is sometimes coated with a photo-sensitive substance and the image of the photographic negative is projected upon it—rather like when an enlargement is made of an ordinary photograph. After developing, the effect is that in the areas where metal is to remain the silk is un-affected, but in the other areas the meshes in the silk are blocked.

When the processed silk screen is placed in the 'printing frame', therefore, ink is forced through it on to the copper surface of the laminate, but since the ink can only penetrate the unaffected areas of silk the original drawing is transferred on to the copper. The ink, again, of course, is of the special 'resist' kind.

Another way of achieving a similar effect involves the transferring of the circuit by a non-photographic method, such as squeezing ink through a cut stencil—using an adapted 'duplication machine'—or, in the simplest case, by painting on by hand.

There are several other 'printing' schemes, some using con-ventional printing blocks and others thin layers of plastics material, but the two detailed are by far the most popular.

The Etching Process

The etching process dissolves away with the greatest possible accuracy those unwanted copper areas outside the lands of the real, wanted circuit. The etching fluid commonly used is *ferric chloride*. This has the effect of dissolving away the unwanted copper, which is then generally lost. However, there are other etching fluids, some of which allow the dissolved copper later to be recovered from the etching bath, and others which have certain cost advantages and give shorter etching times.

The etching action is to some extent affected by temperature and the laminates must be caused to oscillate intermittently—often continuously in mass-production plants—to secure the correct

Fig. 2.8   Retouching a negative "plate" at a printed circuit factory.

etching effect within a predetermined period of time. The strength
of the etching fluid is also checked periodically, and to avoid the
formation of pinholes in the copper lands, and otherwise faulty
etching, the sludge must be frequently cleared from the etching baths.

After the unwanted copper has been removed, resulting in the
base laminate carrying only the copper of the conductors matching
those on the master diagram, the printed circuit boards need to be
cleaned. Hot water removes most of the resist materials, but the
boards generally pass through baths of various cleansing fluids to
remove all traces of the etching fluid, after which they are rinsed in
clean running water and then dried.

Finishing Off

The printed circuit boards as they now appear are in embryo
state and call for one, two or three finishing-off operations. The
most important is the drilling to accommodate the component
leadout wires. This operation is generally semi- or fully-automated,
whereby multihead drills and jigs for specially positioning the
boards to their drilling positions are used.

For separating the boards where a group has been formed on one
'standard' sheet of laminate, a power guillotine is employed; but
to prevent the boards from splintering along their edges when cut,
they are pre-heated by infra-red lamps. This reduces their inherently

brittle nature while they are being cut, but excessive heat can evoke mechanical distortion, so the pre-heating is arranged to take them up to 80deg.C, which is just about right.

Finally, the boards are either *plated* (with solder, silver or even gold) or merely *lacquered* on their copper sides. Sometimes they are both plated and lacquered, depending on the exact requirements. Lacquering (not uncommonly with a soldering flux that dries hard) and plating prevent the copper surfaces from tarnishing, so easing the subsequent problems of soldering.

Plating with silver or gold (or sometimes with nickel, nickel-rhodium or silver-rhodium metals to give a hard surface to any rubbing contacts or edge-contacts on the circuit to reduce wear) is carried out in the ordinary way, in a plating bath, but tinning with solder is performed by a 'rolling' technique to prevent overheating of the laminates. Lacquering is achieved by dipping. There might also be an intermediate process of printing the component numbers or references on the plain side of the boards.

Laminates

Having followed the various processes involved in the design and manufacturer of printed circuit boards all the way through from the original master diagram, it is now possible to fill in some points about the laminate boards themselves.

At one time there was a sharp distinction between the materials used for the 'entertainment', mass-produced type of board—for radio, television and so on—and those used for the more professional, industrial type of board—instruments, computers, station equipment and etc. The first type was almost of synthetic-resin-bonded-paper (SRBP for short) construction, while the second type was of synthetic-resin-bonded-glass-fibre (SRBF for short).

The SRBF has superior mechanical and electrical properties; but although these distinctions still exist, the SRBP type has so improved in recent years that it, too, is currently being used for 'higher grade' applications. However, the more sophisticated SRBF is still being used for top-class applications—in electronics, military and similar applications—where its advantages of greater electrical strength, great resistance to heat and moisture and mechanical strength can be fully exploited. There have been recent developments in this area based on glass epoxy laminates, etc.

There is still another base material designed for ultra high-frequency electronic applications, which is of ceramic nature. This keeps the dielectric losses to a minimum at very high frequencies.

Where flexing of the printed circuit is required, plastics materials such as polyethylene-terepthalate are adopted. These go under such trade names as *Terylene, Melinex, Dacron, Mylar* and so forth. See Fig. 2.9.

Metal Foil

The metal foil, bonded to the base laminate, is almost always electrolytically-prepared copper. Minimum thickness is 0·00012in. (about 3μm), while the most commonly employed 'thickness' is known at '1-oz. foil', which weighs 1oz. per sq. ft. (about 28 grams per square 30 sq. cm) and is approximately 0·0015in. (about 30μm) thick. Use is sometimes made of 2-oz. or even 3-oz foil, having

Fig. 2.9   Example of a flexible type of printed circuit (Bakelite).

respective thicknesses of 0·003in. (76μm) and 0·0045in. (about 0·1mm). These heavier foils are used for high current applications. In rare cases aluminium foil is adopted, and even silver and gold foils have been used in highly critical applications.

Some laminate boards have copper foil bonded on to both sides, allowing the design of a sort of 'two-dimensional' printed circuit board, as is often demanded by very complex electronic circuits. This is shown in Fig. 2.10.

Fixing the Components

It is general practice for the components to be assembled on the plain, non-metallic side of the boards, with the wire leadouts pushed through the holes already drilled in them so that they protrude at the copper circuit side. This sort of mounting is carried out almost entirely by automated machinery in a plant mass-producing electronic equipment. The trend, too, is for the components themselves to be designed relative to the printed circuit board mode of construction. Earlier components used in hand-wired designs are fast disappearing.

There is also an accelerating move towards the use of composite components—such as integrated circuits or 'potted' circuit assemblies —where a complete circuit network—active (i.e. with transistors incorporated) and passive—is embodied into an insulated block 'encapsulation' or even into a housing about the same size as a transistor! Such items are looked at in greater detail in Chapter 6.

Wire Leadouts

Component leadout wires are connected permanently to the printed conductors either by 'dip soldering' or 'wave soldering'. As its name implies, dip soldering involves dipping the assembled circuit board, copper side down, into a bath of molten solder, the temperature of which is controlled by thermostats. Special equipment ensures that the boards are dipped exactly to a pre-determined depth and held in contact with the molten metal for a critical period of time—often about 5 seconds.

This scheme works quite well in practice, but there are several difficulties, such as the possibility of the solder bridging the conductors and overheating of the board components. These are combated by the wave soldering or flow soldering idea, which is now more commonly adopted. Here the technique is that a paddle within the solder bath is actuated from outside to cause a 'wave' of solder to 'wash' the underside of the board.

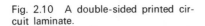
Laminate

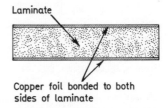

Fig. 2.10 A double-sided printed circuit laminate.

Copper foil bonded to both sides of laminate

The boards are located in a special carriage that traverses the solder bath, and as the board to be soldered arrives at the point of action the solder wave occurs. The soldering operation, involving all the joints simultaneously, is thus performed speedily and efficiently, meaning that the heating effect on the mounted components is reduced. There is also less likelihood of residual solder bridging across the conductors. Some machines pass the board firstly over a flux wave and secondly over a radiant heater, prior to the solder wave.

Printed Components

It is possible to design circuits so that some of the components therein are created by the printed process. For example, a low value inductor can be formed of copper foil spirals on the laminate. Two or more such inductors, in fact, can be connected in series to increase the inductance value, while separate inductors can be coupled mutually or capacitively, giving a transformer effect. Similarly, coils so formed on separate boards can be coupled together, the distance arranged between them determining the coupling coefficient.

This sort of inductor printing is extensively adopted in v.h.f. and u.h.f. filters, as used in television diplexers and triplexers, for example. Initially the inductors are drawn in the correct position on the master diagram, and tables and abacs are available so that the designer may quickly determine with fair accuracy how much inductance his diagram inductors will possess on the finished board.

Capacitors, too, can be made the printed circuit way. The simplest scheme involves leaving an area of foil intact on one side of the board and a similar area, in a corresponding position, on the other side. These foils areas serve as the two capacitor plates and the laminate between them as the dielectric.

Another method involves the use of a very thin plastics base on which copper is uniformly deposited. This is etched away to give the required area related to the capacitance value. The plastics is then cut into lengths, in accordance with the required capacitance value, to yield the 'rolled' cylindrical type of capacitor, but using printed plates rather than the metal foil rolled between paper of the more conventional component.

It is possible to form the static parts of rotary switches by 'printing' the contacts either on the circuit board or, more commonly, on a tough base material. The contacts are coated with rhodium, or similar hard metal, to ensure long life. Even the most complex of switches can be developed in this manner for large quantity production. The base material carries a hole at the switch centre for the insertion of the spindle of the wiper blade and its fixing components.

A form of resistor 'printing' is also practiced, but here the process is somewhat different from the usual techniques. In one scheme a flexible paper or glass-fibre tape is coated with a metallic paint that yields a specific resistance per unit length. The tape is provided with end contacts and finished in synthetic resin. The complete component, comprising the appropriate length of tape to give the required value of resistance, is then integrated into the printed circuit design.

Another method employs a resistive metal—such as nickel-alloy for low ohmic values—in place of the conventional copper foil of the laminate. The metal is etched away in the usual manner, but the length of metal remaining governs the value of the resistor. Highish value resistors are made by zig-zagging the metal lines to provide the greatest possible length in a given space.

CHAPTER THREE

HOW TO MAKE YOUR OWN PRINTED CIRCUITS

LONG PAST ARE THE PIONEERING DAYS when the experimenter in 'wireless' or 'radio'—the term 'electronics' was not then a general part of his vocabulary—constructed his devices and gadgets on the so-called 'breadboard' principal. A smooth piece of 1in. board, not unlike a real breadboard, served as the foundation for the assembly.

Upon this slab of plain wood were assembled the 'radio' bits, comprising massive, screw-down components with large, brass terminals for connecting the wiring, highly scientific-looking (for those days, anyway!) terminal strips and invariably a brightly-polished, ebonite front panel carrying an array of knobs, switches, sometimes glowing valves and more terminals. The wiring, too, was something of a masterpiece, for each length was specially prepared not for the sole function of connecting the components together with the least copper in circuit and thus the shortest routes, but essentially for aesthetic reasons!

Conductors consisting of tinned, square copper rods often carried precision 90deg. bends to fit between the components accurately from terminal to terminal without deviating from the singularly recti-linear wiring formation, very much the order of those days (see Fig. 3.1).

The Metal Chassis

As circuits became more complicated and higher frequencies were used, shortcomings of the breadboard scheme became apparent. For screening and 'earthing' purposes, a sheet of polished copper or aluminium was often applied to the top of the board. This heralded the metal chassis era, and it was not long afterwards that the 'chassis mode' of construction was adopted by manufacturers and enthusiasts alike. Most 'radio' projects then commenced with the construction of a metal chassis.

Early constructors favoured copper for this foundation piece because of its excellent electrical conductivity. Tin-plated steel was next used (it was cheaper), followed by aluminium and more recently die-cast alloy. Die-cast alloy is currently adopted for the construction of enclosed boxes to considerable advantage, especially for the housing and the efficient screening of small printed circuit-sub-assemblies, such as r.f. and a.f. preamplifiers, filters, oscillators, counters, etc.

Fig. 3.1   Reflections of days gone by. This early design for the home constructor (c. 1926) exemplifies the point-to-point wiring and breadboarding of that era (compare with modern breadboarding, Fig. 4.14). Found in the attic of a West Country cottage, the receiver, which is understood to be a John Scott-Taggart design, was in working order apart from an open-circuit r.f. choke.

Experimenters in the v.h.f. and u.h.f. bands discovered that silver-plated copper yields a little more efficiency than unplated metal. This is because v.h.f. and u.h.f. signal currents tend to flow in the first two or three microns of metal surface and that silver is one of the best known conductors of electricity. However, owing to the relatively high cost of silver plating copper sheet and wires, this practice gradually diminished, especially when it was found later that tin-plated steel provided almost the same degree of efficiency.

Printed Circuit Board

The present state of the art is that transistors and integrated circuits are ousting hot valves and wired circuit assemblies. Thus the need for the old-style chassis is dwindling and the printed circuit board is taking over both commercially, as we have seen, and in the amateur fields.

Enthusiasts of the seventies can easily obtain printed circuit type components, transistors and integrated circuits, so the breadboard of today is the printed circuit board—or its equivalent, such as *Veroboard*, detailed in Chapter 4. We shall see now how the enthusiast can make his own printed circuit boards.

Chapter 2 revealed how the manufacturer goes about making printed circuit boards in quantity. The constructor can achieve the same end result by a less complex process, and in many cases a 'one-off' printed circuit board can be created with less effort—and with a greater chance of the finished product working really well—than a conventional wired chassis project. There is also more fun in making one's own printed circuit projects!

Planning the Circuit

The various basic materials and chemicals required for making printed circuit boards can be obtained without too much trouble, as we shall see later, but most of the effort—as with any kind of processing—occurs during the preparing and planning stages. Let us suppose that we wish to build a two-stage audio preamplifier based on a circuit similar to that shown in Fig. 3.2. The first move is directed towards translating the circuit diagram into printed circuit form.

Although this is not particularly difficult, there are several important factors that need to be taken into account if the finished device is to work properly. For example, we must consider the gain factor, and ensure that the input and output parts of the circuit are sufficiently well isolated to avoid the possibility of instability; that is, positive feedback (from the output to input) resulting in the circuit acting as an oscillator instead of an amplifier. We must also ensure that conductors and components carrying high-frequency currents are well separated from those parts of the circuit that could be influenced by them.

Then there is the factor of mains hum that might be coupled from a part of the circuit carrying mains power to a more 'sensitive' part of the circuit, like the base of a transistor. We must also make sure that all the components that need to be returned to 'earth' are catered for, and that the possibility of a common impedance arising in an earth return circuit is totally eliminated by making all the 'earth' as substantial as possible, consistent with the nature of the design.

Other factors that have to be carefully studied include the availability of adequate earth return points on the board and its mounting frame (if used), accessibility of switched connections, need for mechanical fixings, ventilation, effect of vibration, etc.

Translation

The project must, therefore, be thoroughly studied before operations can be commenced, and it is a good plan to 'doodle' with pencil and paper with various possible translations of the circuit diagram to printed circuit form, leading ultimately to a workable plan. To start, the components as physical items need not be drawn into the circuit, it being sufficient to mark them purely as symbols on the printing wiring plan as it progresses.

Fig. 3.3 shows a reasonable translation of the circuit diagram in Fig. 3.2. The shaded areas represent the circuit conductors (the copper foil) which will eventually be developed on the copper side of the board. The component positions are shown by symbols, as also are the holes which will need to be drilled in the board to accommodate the leadout wires. Remember that the components will be mounted on the plain side of the board, as shown in Fig. 3.4.

Now, at this juncture it should be noted that the components can be mounted on the board either vertically or horizontally (horizontal mounting is exclusively adopted in Fig. 3.4). The series of drawings in Fig. 3.5. show horizontal mounting on the left and vertical mounting on the right. The scheme then, is to (a) measure the hole spacing,

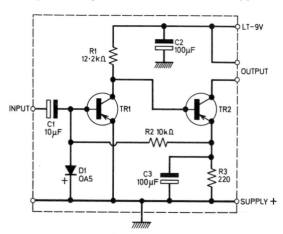

Fig. 3.2 Simple audio amplifier circuit which can be easily made up in printed circuit form.

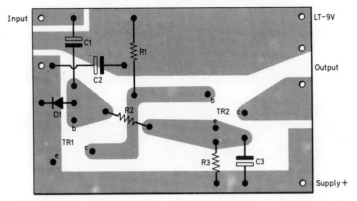

Fig. 3.3   This plan shows how the circuit of Fig. 3.2 can be translated to printed circuit form. Components are indicated by their symbols, but only the plan would be transferred to the copper of the laminate board.

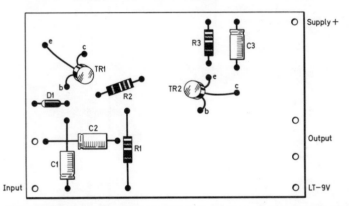

Fig. 3.4   The plain side of the board of Fig. 3.3 with the components in position.

(b) bend the leadout wires, (c) insert the component, (d) cut off excess wire, (e) bend the wire ends and (f) solder the leadouts to the circuit conductors.

Although we have not yet arrived at this stage in the processing of our printed circuit board, it is desirable to have in mind the two mounting methods available so that the layout of the components on the final working plan can be properly dimensioned, as in Fig. 3.4, for instance. The holes for the wire leadouts, too, should be sufficiently spaced to avoid having to bend the wires too close to the bodies of the components, an action that can strain the component elements and show up as a fault condition later when the assembly is put into service.

Grid Dimensions

It can help with the design of complex circuits to draw the plan on a sheet of tracing paper carrying a background grid of vertical and horizontal lines. For professional use transparent sheets of polyester (plastics) film (under the trade name *Mylar*) scribed both vertically and horizontally (giving X and Y axes) with the lines intersecting at fractional or decimal equi-distant points are available. Commonly used grid dimensions for printed circuit applications are eighths and tenths of an inch. (about 3 and 2·5mm).

Fig. 3.6 shows the development of a plan on this sort of material. Firstly, the boundaries of the printed circuit board are clearly

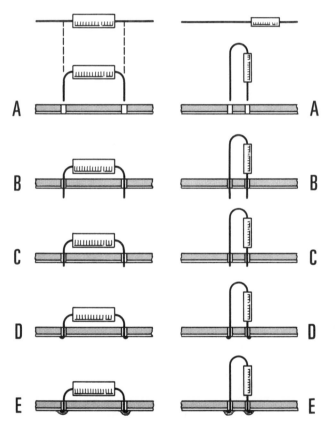

Fig. 3.5 These diagrams show progressive stages in the mounting of components in horizontal or vertical positions.

marked with a black pencil; next the components are drawn on to this background, using the lines as guides; and finally, the required printed wiring is drawn in black pencil or coloured ink. By using this scheme it is easily possible to identify any particular component, hole or conductor by means of X and Y grid reference letters and/or numbers.

Although the general idea is to get the printed conductors to connect the various component parts together as simply as possible and, usually, by the most direct routes, it does not always pay the home constructor to establish a plan that demands the etching away of large areas of copper.

It is possible, of course, simply to arrange the plan so that relatively thin strips of copper connect the various components, but just as

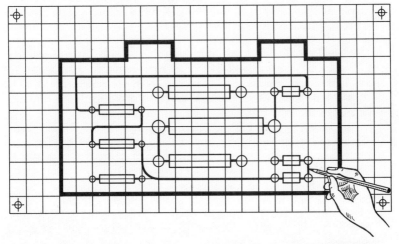

Fig. 3.6   By using a paper with a grid background, the components and wiring can be better planned (See text).

good results can be achieved by leaving fairly large areas of copper, as shown in Fig. 3.3. This applies particularly to the 'earthy' and low impedance areas of the circuit, such as the supply positive and negative areas. These are large areas of copper in the plan of Fig. 3.3.

On the other hand, conductors which are connected to the more 'sensitive' and thus vulnerable parts of the circuit should be minimised as much as possible, and wherever possible a large area 'earthy' conductor should appear between the input and output points of, say, a high gain a.f. amplifier. This is achieved in Fig. 3.3 by the large area of copper isolating the input connection.

Transferring the Plan

Now, once the most desirable working plan has been evolved the problem is to transfer this on to the copper surface of the printed circuit board material. A convenient way of tackling this is simply to place a piece of ordinary carbon paper between the copper surface of the board and the working plan and then carefully trace over the lines of the original plan with a ball point pen. When the design is a very simple one, of course, it can actually be painted direct on to the copper surface with resist ink—but it is always desirable to work from a paper plan, no matter how simple it is.

We must now consider the materials required for the board itself. For the vast majority of applications ordinary SRBP laminate is suitable, and for home-construction applications the copper will invariably be of the 1-oz. foil weight (see Chapter 2). This is generally available in sizes up to 42in. (106cm) by 36in. (91cm) and can when required, be obtained in a size of 50in. (127cm) by 50in. (127cm), which is a large piece of board!

Printed circuit 'kits' are quite useful, not only for the amateur but also for the professional prototype engineer, and these are available from various sources. Apart from other items, later to be mentioned, such kits contain a selection of copper-clad laminate boards of the type just mentioned, but in smaller sizes.

The best idea is to cut the board accurately to size before transferring to its copper side a copy of the working drawing. To avoid the board splintering along its edges when being cut it should be heated—as during printed circuit manufacture—to a temperature of about 80deg.C. In the factory a special cutting guillotine is employed, but the home constructor will find it more convenient to use a fine-toothed hacksaw. However, if the board is fairly large it will have to be held in a vice, protected by two pieces of wood, while being cut.

Cleaning the Board

When the board has been cut and filed smooth along its edges it must be thoroughly cleaned on the copper side before the circuit plan is transferred to it. This is very important, because even the slightest trace of grease (from the fingers, for instance) will impair the etching process; and when the circuit plan has been neatly transferred to the copper surface it is quite frustrating to have to erase it all to clean the copper and then start the whole process again.

Fine pumice powder, with plenty of clean water and rubbing soon puts a good polish on the copper. Indeed, ordinary domestic *Vim* is ideal for this operation, provided it is all removed before the drawing is transferred. Printed circuit kits generally contain a quantity of cleaning powder.

After cleaning the copper in this manner the board should be held under a running tap for several minutes. Surplus water should be shaken off and the board should be allowed to dry thoroughly before the resist is applied. Heated air from a hair drier accelerates this operation. At this stage it is important to avoid the fingers coming into contact with the copper surface; the board should be held edgewise if sufficiently small, otherwise it should be held between clean paper.

The next job is to transfer the circuit plan to the copper and, as already mentioned, this can be done by the use of ordinary carbon paper. When the plan is clearly marked on the clean copper, the areas that are to be left intact as copper conductors must be covered with resist. Referring again to the printed circuit plan in Fig. 3.3, we see that the resist here would be applied over the shaded areas, representing the copper surfaces.

In fact, the plan transferred to the copper would be the same as that shown; but, of course, there would be no need to indicate the component symbols on the transferred plan, for at this stage we are not interested in the components.

Resists

Resist is nothing more than a substance that is unaffected by the presence of the etching acid. It is usually coloured so that it can be clearly seen on the copper surface, and printed circuit kits all contain a small bottle of coloured resist. However, some enthusiasts prefer so-called 'mechanical resists'. These are derived from various adhesive materials, such as Scotch tape and equivalents.

They can be made or purchased in rolls. Some firms also supply precut shapes, such as circles and squares. These resists are stuck firmly on to the surface of the copper, taking care at the intersections and joints to ensure positive adhesion to prevent the circuit from being spoilt by the etching fluid leaking under the joints.

When nothing better has been immediately available, I have employed ordinary masking tape of the kind used by garages for car spraying. This needs to be cut into narrow strips for some of the conductors and specially shaped for others, but it has a very good adhesive surface and is essentially acid-proof. *Sellotape* can also be used.

The lacquer type of paints possess good resist properties, but have the disadvantage of a relatively long drying time. It is essential for the resist thoroughly to harden before the etching is started. There can also be a problem in removing the paint from the finished board. Finger-nail polishes are better for they dry more quickly and are less difficult to remove afterwards. Some of them are also sufficiently coloured.

A common resist is asphaltum. This is an asphalt-base paint which is easily thinned as required with petroleum solvents. Rubber cements, too, make fair resists.

Correcting Errors

Fig. 3.7 shows a small printed circuit board after the resist has been applied to the copper surface with a fine brush. The original working drawing is also shown. With a circuit as small as this, having little detail, it is possible to establish the conductor pattern by painting direct on to the copper, as already mentioned, using the working drawing merely as a guide.

When the resist has thoroughly hardened any errors that might have been made can usually be corrected by gently scratching away the resist with a razor blade or knife. To ensure clear-cut lines round the edges of the copper conductors on the board the resist must be applied with a very steady hand. A flat-edge guide can be used, provided it does not make edge contact with the copper surface. A badly made printed circuit is exhibited by the roughness of the conductor edges.

When the resist is hard, a straight edge and razor blade can be employed to straighten the edges, thereby ensuring that the etched copper, too, will possess similarly straight edges. When stick-on tape strips and shapes are used instead of resist this problem does not arise.

Quantity Production

Before dealing with the etching process it will be instructive to consider how the experimenter can produce small quantities—say, up to 100—of the same printed circuit. He could employ the largest-sized laminate sheet available and paint on to this as many copies— each carboned from the original drawing—as can be accommodated on its surface; or he could use a single master drawing on which the circuit design has been multiplied by hand.

Another interesting scheme involves the drawing of the required circuit pattern full size on white paper or card, using black ink to represent the copper areas to remain on the finished board, and then to photograph this art work to produce a well defined negative. Most

Fig. 3.7 Here is shown the pattern of a printed circuit transferred to the copper side of the board in resist ink.

good quality monochrome films will yield a suitable negative, but a close-up lens for the camera or a camera which itself focuses down sufficiently to fill the negative almost completely with the original drawing will be required.

The film can be exposed out of doors in daylight or indoors in artificial light (using photoflood bulbs), aiming for mild under-exposure, as this will give the best negative for processing the board.

The negative is then put into an ordinary photographic enlarger and the image projected on to the copper surface of the board, which should occupy the position normally taken by the printing paper. One arrangement is to adopt the projected image of the art work as the working 'plan' for painting the resist on to the copper in the ordinary manner, remembering that the bright areas of the display represent (in negative form) the copper that is to remain.

Since the size of the projected image should be as close as possible to that of the original drawing, the art work should carry scaling dots, such as one at each of two diagonal corners. This distance between these two dots should then be accurately measured on the art work, and the same distance achieved between them on the projected image by adjusting the enlarger accordingly. Under this condition the circuit dimensions will have an accuracy determined by that of the optics of the enlarger.

Another arrangement, still using the enlarger and negative, is to coat the copper surface of the laminate with a photo-resist, as described in Chapter 2, and then to consider the coated board as ordinary printing paper, using the projected image to expose it.

The exposure time will, of course, be a function of the image brightness and the type of photo-resist used, but these parameters are readily available from photographic firms dealing in this type of resist.

Glass Negative

If one does not want the bother of photography, the drawing can be transferred on to a sheet of glass—and this also applies to a multiple drawing—using an opaque paint. Clamp the glass sheet and the paper carrying the master drawing tightly together, as in a picture frame, and arrange for a powerful light to pass through from the bottom, so that the lines on the drawing are clearly visible on the glass sheet at the top. It is then a simple matter to re-draw the pattern on to the glass so as to leave the areas where the copper is to remain on the laminate, while obscuring completely those areas that are to be etched away.

This process creates a glass 'negative' of master-drawing-size which in conjunction with photo-resist on the copper surface of the board, can be used directly to expose the sensitized copper by means of a powerful lamp. After exposure, developing is necessary, as already described.

Home Etching

Next comes the etching of the unwanted copper, and whether a small, single circuit is all that is required or whether a quantity of boards are to be produced, certain precautions must be heeded before the operations are commenced. The most frequently used etchant, as it is called, is *ferric chloride*, and to this is sometimes added a small quantity of *hydrochloric acid* to accelerate the etching process. As these fluids are dangerous and corrosive they must never be allowed to come into contact with the skin, with any utensil used for the preparation of food or with clothing or household fabrics. Rubber gloves should be worn.

If the solution is splashed into the eyes, immediately wash them thoroughly with clean, warm water and consult a doctor or hospital with the least delay. Wear protective goggles! Anti-gas goggles, which are still available from ex-Government sources, are ideal for this purpose. Most important: children should never be allowed access to the etching fluid.

If one is proposing to undertake a considerable amount of etching work, an essential aid is a large, plastics tray with a suitable lip. For most jobs, however, a smaller plastics trough or bath is ideal, but the depth of liquid must be sufficient to completely cover the laminate. Printed circuit kits usually come in a plastics box, which can second as the etchant bath. It will be appreciated, of course, that metal in any form must never be used to accommodate the fluid !

The etchant is generally in liquid form in printed circuit kits, but it will be supplied in the form of crystals from a chemist. Warm— never hot water is required to mix the solution in a glass or plastics container.

The best etching temperature is between 37deg.C and 48deg.C, but is not critical so far as the home-constructor is concerned. Excessive temperature is undesirable, but the warmer the solution, the more rapid the etching. A good etchant can be produced by mixing 4-oz. of ferric chloride and 1-oz. of hydrochloric acid with 6-oz. of water.

Agitation

The laminate board carrying the resist pattern of the printed circuit is then dropped into the etchant bath, and gentle agitation of the fluid is desirable while the copper is being dissolved away. The process will take between 5 and 20 minutes (sometimes longer) to complete, depending on the strength of the etchant, its temperature and the thickness of the copper foil.

One scheme for agitating consists of placing a small glass or plastics object beneath the bath, arranged so that it cannot move out of position. Tipping the edge of the bath on one side with a gloved finger will swill the liquid in one direction which, on returning, will tip the bath in the opposite direction, and so on.

Another way is manually to agitate the board in the etchant. This can be achieved by pressing a rubber vacuum 'sticker' on to the plain side of the board before it is immersed in the etchant, then, with a plastic rod extension, it is easily possible to move the board about in the solution from time to time. This technique also allows easy removal of the board, if necessary, during the processing to see how well the copper is being dissolved and whether the process is complete.

Fig. 3.8 shows at (a) several small boards in a bath of etchant, and one carrying a rubber 'sticker' of the kind referred to. (b) shows one of the boards lifted from the bath for examination; here the process has not been completed since some unwanted copper remains.

Professional etchers attain a more speedy result by using large baths, by continuous and forceful agitation of the whole board and by the use of strong solution, with the acid additive.

It is possible to use the solution for continued processing, but this

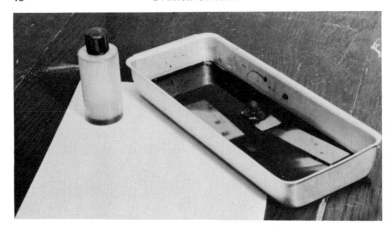

Fig. 3.8 (a)—above—several boards undergoing etching. Note that one of the boards carries a rubber "sticker", facilitating agitation. (b)—below—a partly etched board removed from the etchant for examination.

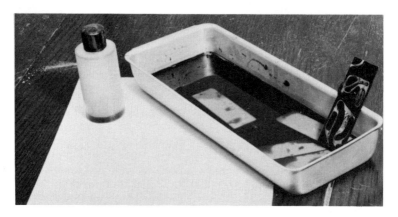

is rarely worthwhile unless it is to be employed again almost immediately. Copper chloride sludge settles out, and particles of this may get into a subsequent bath and result in the formation of dark spots on the copper conductors. Incidentally, a dirty copper surface on a processed board could indicate the transference of grease from the fingers to the clean copper at some time during the processing, and for this reason absolute cleanliness is essential.

The spent etchant must not be poured away down a stainless steel sink, as dark marks will almost certainly be caused. Use an earthenware sink or a toilet bowl and plenty of water.

Finishing-off

When all of the unwanted copper has been dissolved from the plain areas between conductors, the board should be taken from the etchant and then washed in running water for several minutes. This still leaves the resist, which must be removed with a suitable solvent, obtainable from the makers of the resist, and invariably contained in a printed circuit kit.

Most resists, however, can be removed with methylated spirit or with a petroleum-based solvent. After this, the copper surfaces should be polished with the same kind of cleaner (e.g. domestic *Vim*) as was used originally for cleaning the foil.

At this stage it is a good idea to check that the separate conductors are insulated from each other. Where a fair amount of space exists between metal the lack or otherwise of insulation will be obvious but in areas where conductors are closely spaced it is possible for slightly incomplete etching to leave a fine trail of copper between them. This can be quickly revealed by resistance or continuity tests, as shown in Fig. 3.9. In the event of an unwanted inter-connection, it is generally possible to clear the short-circuit by scraping away the spurious copper with a scriber or similar tool.

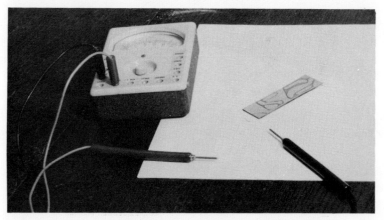

Fig. 3.9   Testing a printed circuit board for short circuits.

The board is then drilled to take the leadout wires of the components. The positions of the holes will be indicated on the master plan, so this can be placed on top of the finished board and a pointed tool used to mark the drilling positions on the copper side. The copper left round the wire terminations must be sufficient to take a $\frac{1}{32}$in. (0·79mm) or $\frac{1}{16}$in. (1·58mm) hole, according to the size and number of the wires to be inserted into it; but this, of course, is determined at the planning stage, as mentioned earlier.

When all the hole positions have been clearly marked, the holes can be made with an ordinary drill, but it must be sharp to prevent the copper lifting from the laminate. For the majority of applications, the hole diameter given by a No. 60 drill is suitable.

Fitting the Components

Finally, the components have to be fitted into their appropriate holes on the board and the leadout wires soldered to the copper conductors on the reverse side. Since the copper has been thoroughly cleaned, there should be no difficulty in getting the solder to run, and it is not usually necessary to tin the copper surfaces before fitting the components. However, if it is decided to tin the copper surfaces prior to the fitting of the components, then it will almost certainly be necessary to go round all the holes with a pointed tool, like a scriber, to clear the solder from them.

Fig. 3.10 The finished board of the previous pictures shown with the components soldered in position.

It is however, important for the component leadout wires to be free from oxidisation and nicely tinned themselves before they are inserted into the holes. This ensures the development of an efficient soldered joint with the least amount of heat. The soldering iron should feature a small, instrument-sized bit, well shaped and tinned; moreover, its temperature should be sufficient to provide rapid fusing of the solder between the leadout wires and the copper.

When soldering the wires of semiconductors it is desirable to isolate the heat from the component by means of a 'heat-shunt'. This can be a pair of pliers or a copper-faced 'crocodile' clip. The heat shunt is attached to the wire of the component being soldered. The picture in Fig. 3.10 shows the reverse side of the printed circuit board of Figs. 3.7, 3.8 and 3.9 after the components were mounted on it and their leadout wires soldered.

Prototype Production

On a more professional basis, prototype engineers, development engineers, etc. can now obtain a self-contained outfit for the speedy production of prototype boards. One such outfit (by Apollo Electronics Limited) incorporates a precision co-ordinatograph designed for quick and accurate production of printed circuit masters, thick and thin film and silk screen masks. The masters may be produced directly from a freehand layout drawing.

Accessories include an exposure unit, etching kit, containing all the necessary chemicals and a supply of copper laminate boards, and a circle tool for scribing circles, arcs and anulli to a radial accuracy of 0·05mm.

CHAPTER FOUR

PRINTED CIRCUIT SUBSTITUTES

IT IS SHOWN IN CHAPTER 3 how the electronics amateur and prototype engineer can process their own printed circuit boards and
design and evolve circuits around them. In this chapter we shall
investigate substitute techniques which, while having a great deal
in common with the printed circuit idea, avoid all of the basic
processing necessary to produce a real printed circuit board.

Details are also given to enable the amateur constructor and
prototype engineer to evolve circuit systems based on these substitutes.
Two substitutes are *Veroboard* and *Cir-Kit*, and we shall commence
with the *Veroboard* technique.

Veroboard Technique

Veroboard is very much of a printed circuit board nature—the
copper 'printing' having already been done at the factory and
basically consists of a synthetic resin-bonded paper laminate with
a thickness dimension of 0·062in. (about 1·5mm) upon which are
bonded a number of copper strips 0·0015in. (about 37µm) thick running the full length of the board, pierced with a regular matrix of
holes for accommodating the leadout wires of the circuit components
(Fig. 4.1).

As we have seen, ordinary printed circuit board might also consist of a similar laminate upon one side of which is bonded a sheet
of thin copper. This makes it the job of the circuit designer to work out
the circuit so that the unwanted copper can be etched away. While
this is not unduly bothersome at mass-production levels, it is time-
consuming and messy so far as the prototype engineer and the home
constructor are concerned.

Moreover, once the copper has been etched it is impossible to
change the configuration of the printed conductors without altering

Fig. 4.1 A piece of Veroboard made of copper strips bonded to a laminate board of specific hole matrix.

the circuit parameters. So unless the finally developed prototype board is likely to lead to fairly large scale reproductions—which is where the printed circuit board really scores—not much advantage is gained by going to all of this trouble. This is especially so now that *Veroboard*—and the *Cir-Kit* system—are available to the home constructor and the professional prototype engineer.

Similar reasoning applies also to items of limited production, for a complex printed circuit board only really substantiates its development costs when it is reproduced in the thousands. A small run of, say, a special amplifier can be based on *Veroboard*, for instance more economically, and with this substitute in particular there is the added satisfaction of knowing that the specification of the device over the small run will remain constant; at least, so far as the parameters of the Veroboard itself are concerned.

It is also relatively simple to arrange the printed copper strips of *Veroboard* to yield the best possible circuit configuration, and in some cases this will simulate almost exactly the theoretical layout of the circuit on paper.

Conductor Strips

The scheme is to utilise the conductor strips as circuit inter-connections, and to join and break the strips where necessary, with respect to the component parts, to secure the most logical circuit 'pattern' on the board. The component wires are passed through the holes of the matrix usually from the blank side of the board (but it is noteworthy that some species of *Veroboard* have conductor strips bonded to both sides of the laminate), cut to the required length at the copper strip side and then soldered to the conductors, exactly the same as with printed circuit boards.

Fig. 4.2 shows at (a) a plug-in module derived of *Veroboard* with the components on the plain side and at (b) the underside of the same module with the component leadout wires soldered to the copper strips. Notice the wire 'straps' on the component side of the board at (a), these serving to interconnect related copper strips to provide the required circuit configuration.

Each copper strip can be regarded as a potential circuit conductor, and in practice it is not unduly difficult to juggle with the components on the board to obtain a good electrical layout, keeping in mind such undesirable factors as unwanted couplings and common impedance connections.

It is best to keep the input and output sides of, say, a high gain audio amplifier to opposite sides of the board, thereby keeping the distance between them at a maximum. This will reduce feedback and instability problems, which might otherwise result in the signal from the output at high-level gaining admittance to the low-level input. These factors of course, are present in all modes of circuit construction, but with *Veroboard* they are often less troublesome than when a circuit is based on point-to-point wiring.

In addition, it is often possible to utilise some of the copper strips as 'earthy' or low impedance conductors to separate strips of higher impedance and carrying signals of greatly differing levels. Further 'screening' can be provided by means of short, metal strips soldered along an 'earthy' conductor separating two high impedance conductors which might be likely to interact signalwise; and, if necessary, such screening can be extended between components on the plain side of the board.

Design Sheets

To assist with the design and development of circuits using their product, *Vero Electronics Ltd.* have produced a number of accessories. One of these is a 'Design Sheet', consisting of two diagramatic drawings of *Veroboard* on a quality tracing paper—one drawing corresponding to the plain side of the board and the other to the circuit side. On both drawings the matrix holes are indicated by dots, and each row of holes is numbered or lettered to facilitate speedy return

Fig. 4.2. A Veroboard "module" with edge-connector fitted (a)—above—
top view showing components on the plain side of the board and (b)—below—
bottom view showing the soldering of the component leadout wires on the copper
strips.

reference to any hole of the matrix. Such a Design Sheet is shown in Fig. 4.3, on which the the plain side drawing shows the components.

When a layout is being designed it is desirable to obtain several prints, and on the top drawing, representing the plain side of the board, to lay out the circuit, while simultaneously marking the lower drawing, representing the copper strip side of the board, the points where the copper strips need to be severed to suit the circuit design.

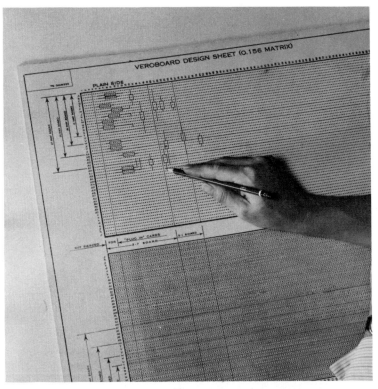

Fig. 4.3 A Veroboard Design Sheet being prepared.

When laying out the components, it is essential to keep in mind their physical size and the minimum number of holes they will span. In this connection there is a useful Component Jig, made in *Traffolyte*, which enables wire terminations of the components (leadouts) to be bent to fit the matrix of the board.

One leadout wire of the component is placed in the hole corresponding to the number of spaces it is required to span, the component

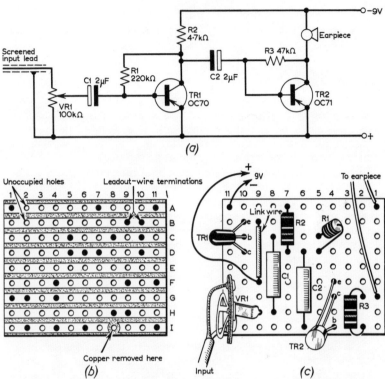

Fig. 4.4 Veroboard construction. Board (b) is prepared to suit circuit (a) and the finished device (audio amplifier) is shown at (c).

is then flattened against the jig and the other wire is bent over a notch at the end of the jig to match the multiple of the board matrix. The design of this jig is based on General Purpose *Veroboard* with a hole matrix of 0·1in. (2·5mm).

Design Example

An example of a very simple *Veroboard* circuit is given in Fig. 4.4, where (a) shows the circuit (a two-stage audio amplifier), (b) the conductor side of the board upon which it is built and (c) the components mounted on the plain side. Notice the hole numbering of the matrix along one side of the board and the lettering along the other side.

These numbers and letters on the board at (b) correspond to those on the reverse side at (c), thereby making it simple to develop and follow a specific design. The black dots on the conductor side drawing at (a) represent holes occupied by the component leadout wires, and these can easily be translated to the top side of the board in drawing (c).

Linking Strips

More complex circuits—even the most complex can be based on a suitable size of board—with higher component densities retain the basic principle of circuit development. It is usually possible to arrange for a central copper strip to serve as the power supply rail and two outside strips as negative 'earthy' rails.

The circuit in such a configuration could then be balanced either side of the power supply rail, especially where 24- or 32-strip board is adopted. It is sometimes necessary to link a part or the whole of one copper strip to the whole or a part of another strip, and this is achieved simply by soldering a wire link between the two strips at convenient holes, so that the link appears at the plain or component side of the board.

The wire link in Fig. 4.4(c), for instance, links hole B9 to hole F9. Sometimes it is desirable to put an insulating sleeve on the wire link to prevent it from shorting to adjacent components or their lead-out wires, though in some designs an uninsulated link wire can constitute a useful 'test point'.

The number of drawings required to develop the final master drawing will depend on (a) the complexity of the device under design and (b) how well skilled the operator is in the art of circuit logic, for this is what such design boils down to. A relatively simple design for the home constructor will probably require no more than one drawing, slight deviations and variations being corrected on the one Design Sheet; but a more complex circuit intended for production runs will generally demand several trial drawings before a good, workable example is eventually evolved.

The positions and references of the components can be silk-screen printed on boards developed for production runs, and once the design of a prototype board has been finally passed for production, complete processing, including silk-screen printing can be handled by the Vero firm if required.

Cutting Tools

As we have seen, the copper strips are cut along their lengths to form the circuit configuration, and to facilitate this operation the Vero Company has developed two types of cutting tools, one for machine application and the other for hand use. These, shown in

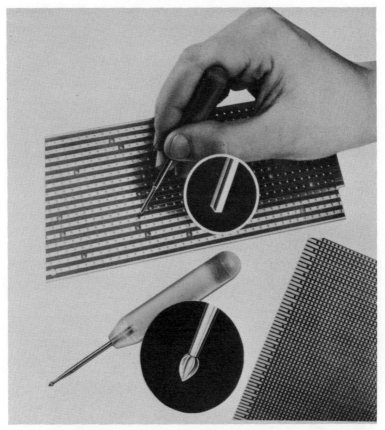

Fig. 4.5 Veroboard spot-face cutters, available for hand and machine use.

Fig. 4.5, are called Spot Face Cutters, and for amateur applications the convenient hand tool is mostly used. The spigot at the working end is located in the appropriate hole and the tool turned clockwise to secure a clean cut along the copper strip.

Another useful accessory for the professional operator is an Assembly Stand which is adjustable to cater for any size of board. The arms are spring-loaded for easy removal and replacement of the board, and the stand permits the operator quickly to reverse the board for component placement and subsequent soldering of the leadout wires.

The first *Veroboard* was of a single basic panel size with holes and copper strips on an 0·2in. (5mm) pitch, which was later extended to a range of board sizes, followed by a range of boards of 0·15in. (3·8mm) and 0·156in. (3·9mm) pitches and finally by a further range of boards of 0·1in. (2·5mm) pitch, which is the matrix constituting the so-called General Purpose type of board.

Boards are thus available in four pitch values—0·2in. (5mm), 0·15in. (3·8mm), 0·156in. (3·9mm) and 0·1in. (2·5mm)—while the matrix can consist of holes pitched equally at one value along both axes or pitched at one value along one axis and at a different value along the other axis, yielding matrices of $0·2 \times 0·2$in. (5×5mm), $0·2 \times 0·1$in. ($5 \times 2·5$mm), $0·15 \times 0·15$in. ($3·8 \times 3·8$mm), $0·156 \times 0·1$in. ($3·9 \times 2·5$mm) and $0·1 \times 0·1$in. ($2·5 \times 2·5$mm). Such matrices related to a wide range of board sizes—based on numbers of rows of holes and copper strips—amount to more than 200 configurations.

As with proper printed circuit boards, *Veroboard* can be obtained with the copper strips roller-tinned soldered to avoid the difficulty of getting good soldered connections on somewhat tarnished copper surfaces, which can happen due to protracted exposure to the air. It can be obtained, too, on an epoxy glass laminate of 0·062in. (about 1·5mm) thickness for more exacting circuits.

REVERSE SIDE

Fig. 4.6 Double-sided Veroboard designed for IC mounting. This picture shows two rows of ICs in TO5 encapsulations at the top and two rows in dual-in-line configuration at the bottom; also the edge-connector used with this type of board.

Fig. 4.7   Double-sided Veroboard with edge-connector fitted accommodating a series of IC TO5 devices with "spreaders".

Double-Sided Boards

There is also a wide selection of boards with copper strips on both sides, those on one side running at right-angles to those on the other side. This is called Double-Sided board, and special boards of this kind have been developed for the mounting of integrated circuits (dealt with in Chapter 6).

Designs are geared to accommodate TO-5 IC packages and dual-in-line devices in their standard forms. These boards are based on the 0·1in. (2·5mm) matrix, and to ensure that the pitch between the termination wires of TO-5 packages is compatible with the hole matrix, 'spreaders' are used between the ICs and the board. With dual-in-line configurations, the copper is removed from around the holes into which the device terminations are inserted, the terminations are then soldered to the copper strips on the opposite side of the board.

To secure connection between the copper strips on both sides, when this is necessary, terminal pins are inserted into convenient holes and soldered to the copper strips to be joined together. Suitable pins are made for this purpose.

The IC boards are also made in plug-in versions, with gold-plated side contacts to ensure low contact resistance, while a special version is available for the dual-in-line devices, on which the copper strips have already been milled to facilitate the direct mounting of the packages without the need for further processing.

Fig. 4.6 shows a Double-Sided plug-in IC board carrying TO-5 packages in two rows at the top—using the 'spreaders' just mentioned—and two rows of dual-in-line packages at the bottom.

Notice the side contacts on the left-hand side of the board. These plug into separately terminated sockets along the length of the edge-connector, also shown in the picture. A similar board loaded only with ICs of TO-5 encapsulation and their 'spreaders'—with the edge-connector fitted to it—is illustrated in Fig. 4.7.

Plug-In Boards

Ordinary *Veroboard* of all pitches, designed for plug-in applica-

Fig. 4.8 A selection of Vero plug-in boards, showing edge-connectors and handles.

tions and carrying 15, 16, 18, 22, 24, 27, or 32 contacts is also made for the prototype engineer and amateur enthusiast. Boards of this kind are depicted in Fig. 4.8, along with a selection of matching edge-connectors. The edge-connectors—which are very important

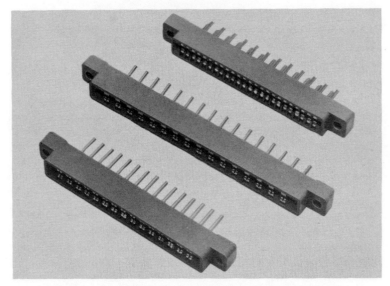

Fig. 4.9 A selection of edge-connectors suitable for Veroboard.

components in contemporary electronics and printed circuit systems
—are shown in greater detail in Fig. 4.9.

Plug-in boards make it possible for both the enthusiast and the
professional engineer to design sophisticated electronic devices based
on the 'module' system from immediately available items, while
avoiding the delay in designing and acquiring printed circuit board
prototypes. A somewhat complex device built on the 'module'
principle—using a single-sided plug-in *Veroboard*—is pictured in
Fig. 4.10.

Associated hardware includes a variety of racks and cases,
including professional-looking instrument cases and the like,
specially designed to accommodate plug-in boards and standard
type boards of various sizes.

Housing Boxes

Other firms manufacture and market cases and boxes in which
Veroboard and, indeed, almost any other kind of printed circuit
board can be housed. These are made of a very rigid aluminium
alloy and carry internal divider slots that will fit either internal
screens or the circuit boards themselves. Thus, a system composed
of several boards can easily be arranged with screening plates
between them as the design may require.

Professional-looking items of electronics can thus be evolved along these lines, and the advanced constructor is now in a position to develop complex test instruments, radio sets, converters, audio amplifiers, microphone mixers and so forth, which not only work up to the standards of factory-made counterparts, but which also look as professional.

The Vero boxes and cases carry a series of edge-connectors along the rear of their compartments so that the circuit sections—built on plug-in boards—can easily be removed for adjustment, repair or replacement. This so-called 'module' idea of system development is increasing in popularity in contemporary electronics at all levels, with encouragement from the computer sector of the industry and with the advancement of integrated circuits. Thus, using ICs, an astonishingly complex item of electronics can be built upon a series of plug-in circuit boards.

To facilitate the insertion and extraction of the boards, insulated handles are often fitted to protrude from the front of the module case. Three such handles are shown in Fig. 4.8, the holes in the boards indicating how they are fixed. Made from a black polycarbonate material, each style is designed to accommodate a small card to identify the board to which it is related.

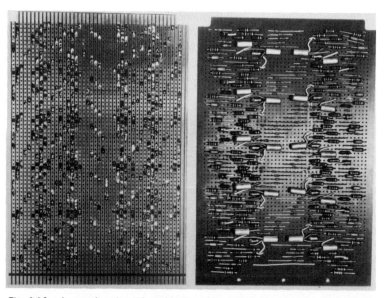

Fig. 4.10   A complex circuit board built on Veroboard, showing the components mounted on one side and the soldered connections to the copper strips on the other side.

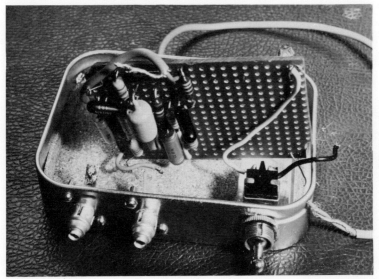

Fig. 4.11 Showing how a Veroboard device (in this case a pickup amplifier) can be mounted in a 2-oz. tobacco tin.

Other Housings

The amateur constructor often devises his own housing arrangement for a small item of printed circuit board equipment, and one idea is illustrated in Fig. 4.11. Here the board is styled into a pickup cartridge amplifier for hi-fi, and the board itself, along with the operating battery, is housed in the 2-oz. (28 grams) tobacco tin. The base of the tin is covered with thin cork (could be rubber) to avoid the conductor side of the circuit board from shorting, while the board is supported at each corner by small rubber grommets.

Another method of mounting small devices which I have favoured over the years is shown in Fig. 4.12. Here the mounting is a standard M-K electrical terminal or switch-mounting box, which is available in two sizes and two colours, cream and brown. Within this type of box are ledges on the sides upon which the board can rest, and with small devices there is room, too, for the battery, switch, sockets, etc. Fig. 4.12, in fact, depicts an r.f. amplifier.

Another system of circuit board connecting makes use of contact pins (called *Varicon Contacts*), designed to suit the matrix pitch, and in one application these can be inserted through the holes from the plain side of the board and retained by soldering to the copper strips. They can provide either single point contacts, or arranged in rows to form connectors for plug-in boards. There are also *Varicon Connectors* which can be related to a design based on the contacts (see below).

Another kind of *Veroboard* is devoid of the bonded copper strips, but instead carries a row of gold-plated contact 'fingers' at one end. This is called *Finger Board*, and these boards or cards, as they are sometimes called, are pre-pierced with 0·052in. (about 1·3mm) diameter holes based on an 0·1 × 0·1in. (2·5 × 2·5mm) matrix.

By using Vero terminal pins it is easily possible to develop a circuit configuration by wiring from pin to pin in relation to the components, whose wire leadouts are also terminated to the pins in accordance with the circuit design. In other words, this is a scheme representative of the old point-to-point wiring techniques, but very much updated!

By using double-side pins—which protrude equally on both sides of the board—it is possible to 'spread out' the circuit so that it occupies both sides of the laminate matrix. Plain boards of this kind—without the contact fingers—are also available and these could be used with the *Cir-Kit* idea, soon to be described.

It is impossible, of course, to detail all of the various types and sizes of *Veroboard*—and accessories—in the short compass of this chapter, but among the popular types available to the enthusiast, the most suitable for general circuit construction are as follows:

Type 42/1503 $2\frac{1}{2}$ × 5in. (6·35 × 12·7cm) 16 copper strips.
      43/1504 $2\frac{1}{2}$ × $3\frac{3}{4}$in. (6·35 × 9·52cm) 16 copper strips.
      45/1507 $3\frac{3}{4}$ × 5in. (9·52 × 12·7cm) 24 copper strips.
      46/1508 $3\frac{3}{4}$ × $3\frac{3}{4}$in. (9·52 × 9·52cm) 24 copper strips.

Cir-Kit Technique

We now come to the *Cir-Kit* way of making 'printed circuit' boards. In this technique the prime component is a length of 0·002 (about 50μm) thick, high-purity copper strip which carries a paper-backed self-adhesive on one side, and the basic idea is that the circuit is actually stuck on to the laminate board by peeling off the siliconised backing strip to expose the adhesive material.

This is a clever scheme and one which works quite well in practice when only a single prototype or the construction of a one-off device is all that is required; however, once the basic circuit has been worked out, and provided it is not unduly complex, reproductions can be generated simply by running through the whole circuit-making exercise as many times as required, provided the time factor is not important!

The copper strips are coated with a lacquer which appears to assist with the soldering; and there are two widths—$\frac{1}{8}$in. (3·1mm) and $\frac{1}{16}$in. (about 1·5mm)—along with 6in. (15·2cm) wide sheets of the material for 'cutting out' the circuit, as explained later.

Fig. 4.12   Here is shown how a small circuit board—Veroboard or ordinary printed circuit board—can be mounted in a standard electrical M-K plastics box.

A circuit can be laid on almost any insulating material which will take the adhesive, but for permanent 'circuit boards' ordinary laminate, either plain or pierced is adopted. The first action is to work out the circuit configuration on a sheet of graph paper, just the same as if one were designing a circuit for etching in the usual printed-circuit-making manner.

This 'master' drawing is placed over the laminate board and the holes required for the component leadout wires are then impressed through the drawing onto the board by a pointed tool or punch—a small hand-operated auto punch is ideal for this. The leadout wire holes are next drilled with a No. 55 or 60 drill.

The copper strip is then applied to the board, following the drawing and using the drilled holes as guides to ensure that the strips run straight from hole to hole. It is desirable to pass the copper strip right across the top of the holes, which will then show as indentations in the copper, after which excess strip should be removed.

It is an easy matter to use a pointed tool to press through the copper into the holes to produce the terminations for the component leadout wires, as with ordinary printed circuit boards. The circuit board is then ready to take the components, which are mounted on the plain side and soldered on the copper-strip side in the usual manner.

An alternative plan is to employ board drilled with a hole matrix. The copper strips are then laid on the board to yield the required circuit formation but in relation to the holes in the matrix which will eventually accommodate the component leadout wires. If several repeats of the same devices are required, the first one can be designed on matrix board as a 'jig' for drilling the undrilled boards of the remainder of the run—using only those matrix holes, of course, that have been arranged to take the component leadout wires.

Cir-Kit is available on 100ft (30·4m) spools in both widths, while the sheet material is sold in packs of five sheets in 12in. (30·4cm) lengths. Kits are also available; Kit No. 1 containing 12in. (30·4cm) of 6in. (15·2cm) sheet, 25ft. (7·6m) of strip in both widths and three 6in. × 12in. (15·2 × 30·4cm) laminate boards; and Kit No. 2 containing 48in. (122mm) of 6in. (15·2cm) sheet, 100ft (30·4m) of $\frac{1}{8}$in. (3·1mm) strip, 200ft (60·8m) of $\frac{1}{16}$in. (1·5mm) strip, five 6 × 12in. (15·2 × 30·4cm) laminate boards and a 'craft knife', with a spare blade, for cutting the conductors.

Applying the Strip

In practice, the strip is applied to the board rather like applying *Sellotape*, for example, and more or less the same rules apply, especially those of cleanliness of the board to which the material is to be stuck and the fingers; in fact, handling of the adhesive surface of the copper is undesirable, as this can severely impair the efficiency of the adhesion due to the natural oils from the fingers contaminating the adhesive prior to fixing. When applying the copper, therefore, it is best to employ a larger than needed length so that the excess can be cut off, thereby ensuring that the ends have the best possible adhesion efficiency.

It is a simple matter to press the strip on to the surface of the board and run back over it with the finger nail to remove any slight kinks, and a board fully processed appears to possess all of the characteristics of a well made amateur printed circuit board, derived by etching technique.

The big advantage of *Cir-Kit* is that no chemicals are necessary to produce a circuit whose efficiency is equal to that provided by ordinary etching processes; moreover, there are no restrictions to layout, and alterations can be easily made both during and after completion of the circuit design. It is also possible to develop a complex circuit on both sides of the laminate to give the double-sided printed circuit board effect.

Although it is possible to process a bend of a small radius, a degree of kinking tends to occur at the radius, which can spoil the appearance of the finished circuit. This can be overcome by avoiding bends altogether and instead butt one length of copper strip against that of the other which requires connecting, applying a blob of solder at the point of interconnection.

As already mentioned, soldering is a simple matter, but there is a tendency for the adhesive to melt from the heat of the soldering iron; however, this is only of a temporary nature, the bonding restoring as the copper cools off. After soldering, it is best to re-press the copper strip onto the board to ensure a long-lasting copper to laminate bonding.

Cutting the Strip

For the best results a very sharp knife should be used for cutting the strip; this gives a much better edge than tearing, and is easier to process. If alterations to the circuit become necessary, they should be handled as soon as possible after fixing the strip, since the bonding efficiency improves with age and the heat of soldering accelerates the aging process. Care must be taken when soldering small lengths of the strip as the softening of the adhesive due to the heat concentrated into a short length of conductor can cause a change in position.

For large currents the wider strip should be used, of course, and as a rough guide the $\frac{1}{8}$in. (3.1mm) strip will handle a 5-ampere load with a temperature rise of less than 6deg.C above ambient under average conditions.

Using Sheet Material

Now let us see how the 'sheet' material is employed. This is particularly useful where the component density is very high. The entire area of the board which is to carry the circuitry is covered with a sheet of *Cir-Kit*, taking care when removing the backing paper to avoid contamination of the adhesive, and pressing the copper down very firmly and smoothly all over the board. This results in a piece of copper-bonded laminate, rather like that designed for etching, but far more versatile, since the unwanted copper can easily be removed by hand, without the etching process demanded by ordinary copper-bonded laminate board.

If the 'master' circuit has been drawn on a piece of tracing paper, then it can easily be carboned on to the copper surface or, alternatively, the outlines of the lands, connectors and so forth can be drawn directly on to the copper with an HB pencil. Once the circuit configuration is on the copper, the holes for the component leadout wires should be drilled through the copper and laminate, and finally the copper surface can be cut along the lines indicating the required lands, and the unwanted copper carefully prised off. If done properly, the result will be virtually the same as obtained by the do-it-yourself etching process, detailed in Chapter 3.

It is also noteworthy that *Cir-Kit* is useful for repairing existing printed circuit boards and for providing flexible couplings between two items of equipment or two circuit boards. It can also be applied round the edge of a board for connecting purposes and a sheet of it can be used for screening between adjacent circuit boards. Indeed, I have also found it useful for improving the screening of some television receivers, applying it to the inside surfaces of the cabinets when line timebase radiation interferes with radio reception, especially when a transistor portable is operated close to a television receiver.

It is also useful in hi-fi and audio for screening against radio breakthrough and hum, under certain conditions. This material would appear to have a number of valuable applications in electronics generally. It is designed and made by Peak Sound (Harrow) Ltd., but like *Veroboard* is available from any of the usual component suppliers.

Other Substitutes

There are other printed circuit substitutes, including matrix boards and panels by various firms, one being the well known Radiospares Company which specialises in components for the laboratory worker and service technician. This board can be used in conjunction with *Cir-Kit* in the manner already described. It can also be used with connector pins, like those sometimes used with *Veroboard*. Further, it can be used with 'eyelets' which fit into the perforations of the board. It is then generally called 'eyelet board' and is, indeed, sometimes specially made for this application.

The eyelets act as conductor and component terminations, and some species, in fact, are equipped with soldering tags. It is thus possible to produce a quasi-printed-circuit-board assembly by soldering the component leadout wires to the eyelets and connecting ordinary wire between the eyelets to simulate the printed circuit wiring. This works quite well in practice, and is useful for prototype work. Another is 'chequerboard' by Circuit Integration Ltd. This consists of a series of bussed sockets on an 0·25in pitch.

Prototype 'Breadboards'

For prototype and experimental activities in general solderless

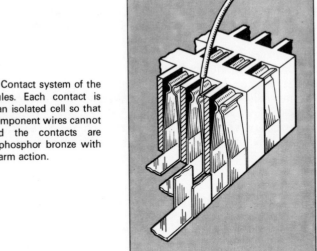

Fig. 4.13 Contact system of the *DeC* modules. Each contact is located in an isolated cell so that adjacent component wires cannot touch, and the contacts are formed of phosphor bronze with long lever-arm action.

'breadboarding' is becoming popular. This is a system whereby the components can be engineered into the required circuit configuration without the problems of soldering and desoldering. A number of breadboarding systems are available, some essentially for IC applications and others suitable for both ICs. and discrete components.

A system which I have found very successful for speedily composing experimental circuits is that produced by S.D.C. Electronics (Sales) Ltd. of 34 Arkwright, Astmoor Industrial Estate, Runcorn, Cheshire. This is known as *DeC*. It consists of a range of modules made of plastics with suitable electrical characteristics.

Each module consists of a 'breadboard' arrangement with the top surface perforated with a hole matrix. Beneath this matrix, and enclosed by the 'breadboard' panel design, are parallel rows of contacts in pre-arranged bus-bar formation, rather like a general purpose wiring board. The bus-bar pattern is indicated on the matrix surface by raised lines, and each perforation lines up with an isolated contact set.

Thus internal connection is made to the leadout wire of a component pushed into a perforation (Fig. 4.13). Component wires of any diameter up to a maximum of 0·04in (1mm) can be accommodated, and the wiping action on insertion and withdrawal of a wire keeps the contacts clean and resistance low.

The bus-bar principle (similar in effect to the copper strips of *Veroboard*, for example) allows the development of any circuit configuration merely by plugging in the component wires to appropriate bus-bar circuits and linking together two or more bus-bars should the circuit so require. Fig. 4.14 shows the general idea of a component assembly established on an *S-DeC* (see later).

The panel carrying the potentiometer is supplied with an *S-DeC* pack. This slips into suitable slots located on one of the long sides of the *S-DeC*. Moreover, all modules are designed for linking together, allowing breadboarding areas of any desired size to be produced.

The matrix of perforations is numbered, the *S-DeC* module, for example, featuring 70 holes and hence contact points, each one numbered. The hole/contacts are arranged in two integrated panels, each one having 7 parallel rows of five connected contact points.

ICs are accommodated on adaptors or 'carriers' designed to accept the device packages either by soldering or by insertion into an appropriate IC socket, which forms an integral part of the carrier. *DeC* modules are also available with IC sockets as an integral part.

The IC. carriers will accommodate all types of IC packages (up to 20 leadout wires). They push directly into the appropriate *DeC* modules, and correct orientation is established by a 'polarising'

Fig. 4.14 Array of components assembled on an *S-DeC* module with control panel in position. Springs are used to connect conductors to items like potentiometers to avoid soldering, and the circuit is established merely by plugging the component wires into holes of the matrix.

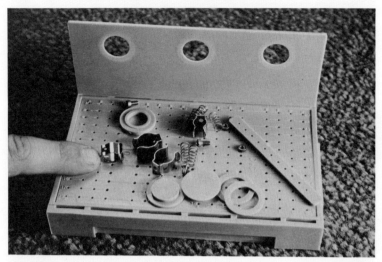

Fig. 4.15 *T-DeC* "breadboard". This has an IC station at centre and matrix hole spacing of 5mm to facilitate mounting the latest short-lead devices. Accessories are shown on top of deck.

pin. The carriers are available either 'plain' or with appropriate sockets attached. The 'plain' versions incorporate a printed circuit board on to which the IC packages may be soldered. The carriers *with sockets* have IC sockets permanently fixed to the same type of board.

The various versions of *DeC* modules are *μ-DeC*, *T-DeC* and *S-DeC*; *μ-DeC* contains two 16-lead DIL sockets (for the IC carriers) in addition to the matrix system allowing it to cater also for discrete components. This is the 'B' version. The 'A' version is similar, but designed more for general purpose applications. Special 'B' versions, with IC sockets as part of the *DeC* module, can also be made available.

μ-DeC 'A' has 208 contact points, 3 bus-bar rows of contacts (16 connecting points per row) across the module, two independent panels of 20 rows of contacts (arranged in 10 pairs, 4 contacts per row), is suitable for use with standard IC carriers (allowing the accommodation of all IC packages), has a 'polarising' pin for each IC carrier and a typical capacity of four 10-lead TO5 stations or two DIL stations.

T-DeC (Fig. 4.15) has one IC station at the centre of the module and is thus intended essentially for use with discrete components or for linear IC applications involving also significant use of discrete components. It has 208 contacts in 38 rows with 5mm separation

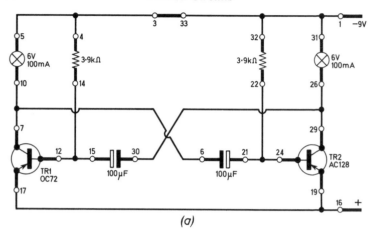

(a)

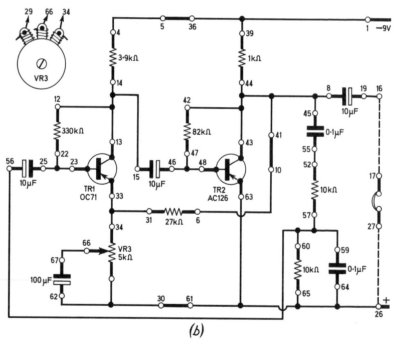

(b)

Fig. 4.16 Example circuits based on the *DeC* "breadboard" system, (a) Electronic flasher and (b) Wien network oscillator. The numbers correspond to those on the matrix, all circuits being based on *S-DeC*. Conductors in thick lines are those on the components or "links" such as that between 3 and 33 at (a), while the thin lines represent the internal bus-bar connections.

between them, thereby enabling the latest short-lead devices to be inserted directly into the contacts. Typical capacity is six to ten stages of discrete circuitry and two TO5 stations or one DIL station, with 'polarising' IC carrier locations. μ-*DeCs* and *T*-*DeCs* interlock via dovetailed sections of the module walls.

S-*DeC* is particularly suitable for educational purposes, and in this connection it is noteworthy that S.D.C. Electronics (Sales) Ltd. has published an 'Experiment Guide' book which, in astonishing detail, describes the technical features and characteristics of a wide range of circuitry which can be produced on the *DeC* module principle.

The *S*-*DeC* Unit Pack also includes a small booklet of circuits along with the *S*-*DeC* module and control panel as shown in Fig. 4.14. Examples of the circuits are given in Fig. 4.16, the numbers corresponding to the matrix holes.

Accessories include small springs for connecting wires to the soldering tags of items like potentiometers (Fig. 4.14), pilot bulb holders, tuning capacitors, etc., plug-terminated 'patching links', component trays, 1mm plugs which fit the holes of the matrix, dips, washers, perforated strip and 'blanks' for unused panel holes.

CHAPTER FIVE

SERVICING PRINTED CIRCUIT EQUIPMENT

PRINTED CIRCUITS AND TRANSISTORS signify the new generation of electronics. Electronic engineers and technicians of the preceding generation were concerned essentially with point-to-point wiring in equipment containing thermionic valves as the active devices, and a very high degree of proficiency was developed in the general servicing of that kind of equipment.

One advantage of point-to-point wiring from the servicing aspect is the ease by which the circuit connections can be traced from component to component; another is the relative lack of complications involved in replacing defective wiring and components. Many technicians who studied the arts of servicing during the valve era do not always find it particularly easy to settle down to transistorised equipment built upon printed circuit boards and modules.

With this in mind one large manufacturer of radios and television sets for a while opted out of printed circuit designs in favour of point-to-point wiring. Receivers of this kind are popular with technicians of the 'old school', even though in part they employ transistors, but the new generation technician might well consider them in a retrogressive light!

Contemporary Design

The vast majority of domestic electronic products handled by the contemporary technician, however, are based upon the printed circuit board—or module—design, and most of them also feature transistors instead of valves.

Already some television models, monochrome and colour, are fully transistored, and in a few years time valves will disappear altogether from this class of equipment, as they have to date from radios and hi-fi amplifiers. It is noteworthy that the manufacturer just mentioned has returned to printed circuits.

It is essential, therefore, for today's technicians to know exactly how to handle the servicing problems associated with printed circuit equipment. From the basic fault diagnosing point of view the principles involved differ little between equipment employing point-to-point wiring or printed circuit wiring. However, with point-to-point wiring it is usually not too difficult to check a suspect component simply by substituting with a replacement known to be in good order.

Moreover, since equipment so wired mostly features valves, a suspect valve can be likewise tested. Such testing schemes rarely lend themselves to printed circuit equipment for the main reason that neither passive nor active components are particularly easy to extract from a complex printed circuit board assembly without damaging the printed circuit conductors or adjacent components.

Of course, when a faulty part has been located it is necessary to remove it and solder in a replacement; but one of the arts required for the servicing of printed circuit equipment is to know almost conclusively that the component is faulty before it is removed. Others are to know how to remove a defective component with the least damage to the printed circuit board and associated components and how to install the replacement component.

Relating the Circuit to the Printed Wiring

These aspects of servicing will be considered in detail later; but first let us look at one or two servicing procedures connected primarily with the printed circuit board itself. When we have an item of defunct printed circuit equipment in front of us it helps considerably to know the layout of the circuit so that the various components and their connections can be quickly and accurately identified.

Fig. 5.1 gives the circuit of a portable radio set (Roberts Model R303), the design of which is based upon a printed circuit board. If we have merely this circuit and the faulty set, quite a lot of time can be expended in relating the connections shown on the circuit diagram to those printed in copper on the board itself.

It is possible to do this, of course, and is indeed necessary, if a more speedy way of identification is not available. A good way is first to locate a transistor or transformer, say, on the circuit diagram and then to associate it with the physical component on the board, after which the connections to the base, emitter and collector can be located reasonably quickly.

Many printed circuit boards have component reference numbers printed by the side of the components on the plain side of the board, thereby enabling even small components, like resistors and capacitors, to be located first on the circuit diagram and then on the board

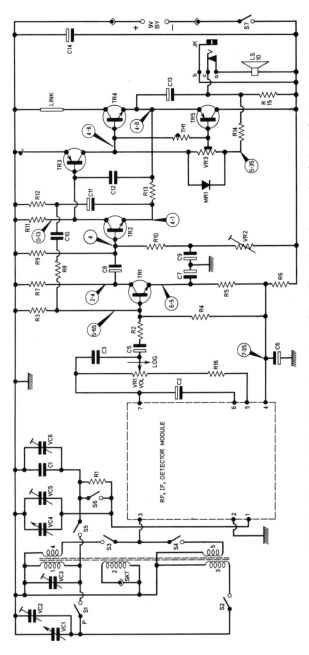

Fig. 5.1 Theoretical circuit of transistored portable radio set based on a printed circuit design.

itself, and from these the printed wiring to the other associated components can be traced.

Although all this might sound fairly straightforward a number of problems can be involved. For example, the printed circuit board is not uncommonly clamped or screwed to a metal frame so that only the plain, component side of the board is accessible or visible. Thus, while the components can be readily identified, the printed circuit cannot.

Moreover, if the circuit side of the board is accessible and visible it is not always easy to trace the copper wiring from component to component unless the laminate is transparent. This means that the board has to be continually turned over from the component side to the printed circuit side and back again, repeatedly, to discover the route taken by the circuit under examination.

This is made exceedingly difficult on complex boards carrying

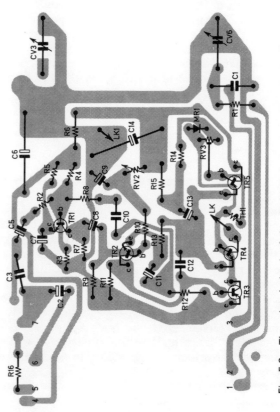

Fig. 5.2 The printed circuit of the theoretical circuit in Fig. 5.1, showing the position of the components on the board. The board is viewed from the foil side, with components shown as seen through the board.

a large number of closely grouped components, for it is all too easy to confuse the identity of leadout wires and printed conductors. It is thus necessary to start the exercise all over again, often with equally as fruitless results!

One way of solving this problem—assuming that the printed circuit side of the board is accessible—is to set up the equipment on the bench vertically so that one is looking at the side of the board carrying the components. Now, by applying a bright light (bench light, for instance) to the printed circuit side, behind the equipment, a distinct outline of the printed circuit will be seen on the component side of the board, and in this manner the circuit conductors can be traced to the components with the least effort.

The best idea, of course, is to have at hand a plan of the printed wiring, showing the component connections, as well as the circuit diagram of the equipment being serviced. Fig. 5.2 shows the printed circuit of the circuit diagram in Fig. 5.1, revealing the simplicity of relating the physical circuit to the theoretical circuit. The majority of service manuals dealing with printed circuit equipment contain plans similar to that shown in Fig. 5.2. as also do *Service Charts* published by Trade Papers, from which Fig. 5.2 was taken.

Some boards have interconnections to associated boards or modules, and these are often identified by numbers or by a letter/ number code. For example, the numbers 1 to 7 in Fig. 5.2 correspond to the similarly numbered terminal points of the i.f. module located on the left hand side of Fig. 5.1.

Poor Soldering

Damage can be caused to printed circuit boards and their components by bad and incorrect soldering techniques and by the use of unsuitable soldering instruments. As this is such an important aspect of the servicing of printed circuit equipment, let us divert for a while and consider the operation in detail, while also looking at some of the more recent soldering aids.

It has been suggested that poor soldering can cause trouble in electronic equipment more frequently than failures of the components themselves. Many servicing men will, indeed, fully agree with this suggestion, especially when they recall the many hours spent during their careers in tracing such symptoms as 'intermittency', 'crackles', 'fizzles' and the like, ultimately cleared merely by resoldering a defective joint – often referred to as a *high resistance joint* or *dry joint*.

Again, a perfectly innocent-looking joint can lead to the condemnation of numerous good components, since the removal of a suspect for test often completely ruins it—and sometimes a component has to be deliberately crushed to extract it from a printed circuit board, as we shall see.

A joint from the surface may appear perfectly sound, yet beneath the well-formed blob of solder may exist substantial electrical resistance between the two conductors, which should be 'linked' as one. A perfect joint occurs only when the solder is induced to flow over the conductor surfaces so as to integrate the molecules, and for this both metals being soldered have to be of the correct temperature.

A joint with a relatively high resistance—as distinct from a definite open-circuit, of course—will have developed across it a voltage due to current flowing through it. In a d.c.-only circuit this will result in a loss of power and overheating of the joint, while in an a.c. or signal-carrying circuit a signal voltage will develop across the joint and often be reflected to other, possibly low-level and critical circuits, causing symptoms of instability, like oscillation and motor-boating.

When the joint in such a circuit has a varying resistance, the signal voltage fluctuates and an interfering voltage or current is superimposed upon the normal circuit voltage or current. These effects are sometimes responsible for the intermittent 'crackles', 'fizzles' and similar disturbances in audio, radio and television equipment.

Fluxes and Solders

Now, to achieve an efficient soldered joint the surfaces to be joined must be perfectly clean and free from oxides, which are very thin non-metallic films covering all metal surfaces, resulting from the action of the oxygen in the air on the metal.

Although the plating on the metals used in electronics, like copper wire, soldering tags and pins, etc. reduces some of the problems in obtaining a perfect soldered joint, since it inhibits the long-term formation of oxides, it is still necessary to make sure that the surfaces are free from grease and dirt and that they are treated with a flux during the soldering process.

Flux—sometimes called a 'wetting agent'—prevents the build-up of oxide when the metals are heated by the soldering iron, for the heating action accelerates the oxidising processes. The nature of the flux is determined by the kind of metals to be soldered, but in almost all areas of electronics a resin flux is used because of its non-corrosive properties (also see page 104). Before the advent of resin fluxes an acid was not uncommonly used as the wetting agent, and one can well imagine the long term corrosive influences that this had on the copper interconnecting wires and soldering tags!

Solders used in contemporary electronics carry their own fluxes in the form of a core or cores of activated resin. The melting point of the solder is also important, and there are numerous solders with melting point temperatures ranging from about 150deg.C to 250deg.C. In addition there are high and low melting point solders, but for electrical and electronics applications solders with melting temperatures as just mentioned are mostly used.

They are composed of specific ratios of tin and lead, and those in common use, which are in wire form with activated resin cores to yield the correct proportion of flux, have tin/lead ratios ranging from 60/40 to 20/80. Resin-cored solder is available in a variety of 'wire' diameters.

There is also a type that embodies a special copper-based ingredient for reducing the wear of the copper bits of soldering irons. This type is particularly popular with servicing technicians, for its continued use means that the bits not only last longer but also require less frequent cleaning. A solder of this kind is called *Savbit* and is made by Multicore Solders Limited.

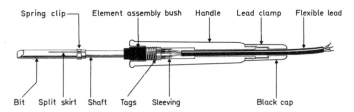

Fig. 5.3   The elements of a miniature solder iron of the kind used for servicing printed circuit equipment (Antex Limited).

Iron Types

Before proceeding on to the actual process of soldering let us have a look at some of the latest soldering irons—or *soldering instruments*, as they are now more correctly called. Printed circuit boards and microelectronics have encouraged the demand for a new kind of miniature soldering iron of a size and weight compatible with the nature of the work.

A truly miniature iron weighs only two or three ounces, thereby giving precise finger tip control, essential for small, delicate circuits, coupled with the minimum of operating fatigue. Such irons are available in power ratings ranging from 8 to 40 watts; there is an even smaller species—referred to as 'sub-miniature'—with ratings from about 6 to 12 watts.

Most irons are designed for use on standard 240V mains supplies, but varieties are available for use on low voltages, derived from the mains supply via a step-down transformer. Alternatively, this sort of iron can be run from a 6 or 12-volt accumulator, and are thus handy for field use, away from a source of mains power.

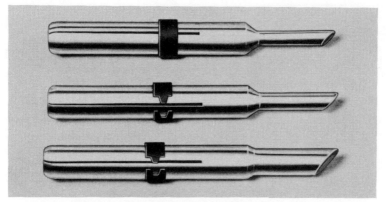

Fig. 5.4   Selection of interchangeable "spade" bits.

Several factors have to be taken into account when choosing a soldering iron, including (i) the available powering voltage; (ii) heat capacity, as governed by the size of the joints, (iii) bit temperature for the nature of the work and (iv) dimensions and shape of the bit, which is the business end of the iron. Fig. 5.3 shows a sectional view of a sub-miniature soldering iron by *Antex Limited*, Model B, in which the various parts of the iron are clearly revealed.

This type of iron—as with similar irons of different makes—is designed to take different sizes and shapes of bit, and for the Antex Model B iron, for instance, 15 different bits are available, interchangeability being achieved by the design of the hot end of the iron and by each bit being made with a split skirt section arranged to be held tightly in thermal contact with the iron shaft by means of a spring clip.

Three bits of different working size to the Antex pattern are shown in Fig. 5.4. These are for the G range which load to 18 watts on main voltages (110 to 240V). The B range load is 12 watts on low voltages (6 to 28V), but both styles weigh only 1oz. (28 grams) less lead. Heat/time curves for the two ranges are shown in Fig. 5.5, (a) for the B models and (b) for the G models. The No. 1020 bit pertaining to curve (b) has a tip dimension of 2·3mm. Clearly, the mass of the tip will influence the curve, and we shall see later that the

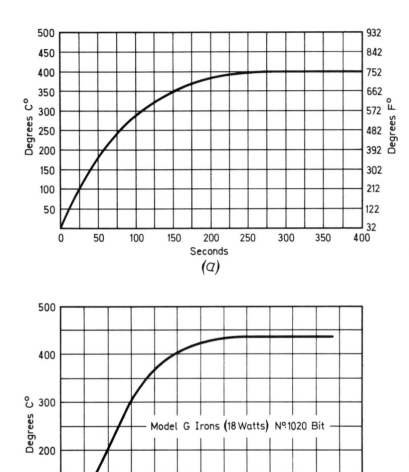

Fig. 5.5 Heat/time curves for Antex irons. (a) for the 12-watt, low voltage model and (b) for the 18-watt, mains-powered model.

bit must be carefully chosen to match the kind of soldering work in hand.

A technician whose work takes him into the field often favours a complete, self-contained soldering kit of a convenient size to fit easily into his tool box, and such a kit by Antex is shown in Fig. 5.6. This contains a miniature type CN240, 15-watt iron, two nickel-plated spare bits of 2·3mm and 4mm along with the 4·7mm bit in the iron, a means for producing a heat-shunt—explained later—and a small reel of resin-cored solder. The CN240, incidentally, is another 28-gram iron rated at 240 volts, and has a length of 16cm (a mere 6·29 in.).

Another extremely popular range of 'soldering instruments' is the 'A' range by *Adcola*. Fig. 5.7 depicts an 8-in. (20·3cm) instrument from that range. It loads at 19 watts yielding a standard temperature of 340deg.C and is available in any voltage between 6 and 7V and 230 and 250V. It is a little heavier than the really miniature models, weighing 4·5oz. (127 grams) but, like the others, has facilities for bit interchange.

Supply Voltage

There are many other types of soldering iron, some of which are mentioned later in connection with other soldering (and desoldering) aids, including fast-heating gun irons. For the moment, however,

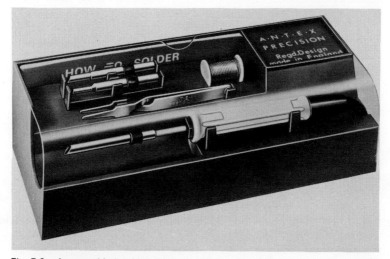

Fig. 5.6   Antex soldering kit containing miniature soldering iron, two spare bits, small reel of solder and heat shunt.

Fig. 5.7   Miniature mains-powered iron (also available in low voltages) by Adcola.

let us look at the parameters which govern the choice of an iron. It is obviously important to ensure that the iron chosen suits the available supply voltage, and it goes without saying that a low voltage model must never be connected to the mains supply. The converse, of course, would simply result in a cold iron!

Low voltage irons must only be connected to sources capable of providing the required power, sometimes for quite protracted periods. Care should be taken to avoid connecting a low voltage iron to a mains transformer which is insufficiently large to withstand the continuous loading. This would quickly overheat the transformer and precipitate early failure.

Likewise a battery of adequate capacity must be employed when battery working is contemplated, and to avoid excessive volts drop—and an iron which fails to heat sufficiently—long connecting wires (on low voltage models) should not normally be used. If operation remote from the power source cannot be avoided, however, heavy, low resistance cables must be adopted.

Size of Iron

The size of iron is determined by the size of the joints to be processed, and in production work, where several thousands of joints are made daily, it is often desirable to over-rate the iron, rather than match the loading exactly to the joint, so that the bit temperature is maintained from joint to joint.

Obviously, the larger the bit (the more metal mass it contains) the more it will act as a 'heat reservoir', resulting in a greater heat reserve for continuous jointing. Where only an occasional joint is made, though, a smaller iron—one which just about matches the nature of the work—can be employed successfully.

It is essential for the bit temperature to be sufficiently high to allow easy flow of the solder on the metal conductors, but not so high as to cause the resin flux to burn or char. It will be understood, of course, that whenever an iron bit contacts the work piece a loss of bit temperature results due to the transfer of heat from the bit to the conductors being soldered. This means that the bit temperature must always be greater than that required to melt the solder.

A basic rule worked out by Antex is that the bit temperature should be about 100deg.C higher than the melting point of the solder—or about 150deg.C higher for continuous soldering. Temperatures approaching some 200deg.C above the solder melting point, however, might be necessary for really speedy soldering, depending on the nature and size of the jointing metals. Soldering irons with larger bits than those associated with the small and miniature types of iron can usually run at lower temperatures owing to the heat reservoir action of the mass of metal.

It is also noteworthy that the temperature of the bit is related to its tip dimension—the smaller the tip, the lower the required temperature for a given wattage loading. However, it is essential for the tip dimension closely to match the size of the joint being soldered. If the tip is much smaller than the joint metal it will undergo excessive cooling, thereby impairing the solder flowing action, while if it is much larger than the joint there is the danger of the heat damaging any adjacent conductors, insulation and components.

Bit Efficiency

The efficiency of a bit is related to its physical dimensions—as well as to its composition—and for maximum efficiency the heating shaft or element of the iron should make the maximum of thermal contact with it and exist well up towards the tip end. As this design cannot always be achieved, and because it makes it difficult to secure bit interchange, the length of the tip proper should be as short as possible, consistent with the jointing requirements, from the bit shank to the tip end, while the shank itself should possess as much metal mass as practical, consistent with the wattage loading of the iron.

The majority of straight bits—sometimes called spade bits—are designed with a chamfer between the shank and the tip. This permits the working surface of the tip to be applied flat against the jointing metals, while the iron is held at an angle, a feature which makes it possible to solder right into the joint without the bit burning adjacent wires and components. Two other popular bits are the chisel and angle, illustrated along with the spade bit in Fig. 5.8.

Owing to the excellent heat conductivity of copper, a bit made of this metal is the most efficient. Sadly, bits composed of pure unplated or untreated copper have a limited life due to pitting and scaling. Thus, to keep the working tip flat and clean constant filing is necessary, an action which quickly reduces the dimensions and makes bit replacement essential. This applies particularly to miniature bits which, to cater for the heat loss, have to be run at relatively high temperatures.

Large irons are less affected in this way because the large bits store more heat and can thus be run at a lower continuous temperature. The bits of small irons, therefore, are commonly copper plated with iron, nickel or chromium or made of copper alloy, such as berylium-copper or chromium-copper, with cadmium coating to inhibit scaling. For very small work nickel bits are sometimes used, but since these have an efficiency only about one-fifth of copper they have to be run at high temperatures; however, they are long-lasting.

Sometimes the shank is made of coated copper and the tip of iron or nickel as a means of improving the efficiency. Many bits used for electronics and printed circuit work, though, are copper based with a nickel or iron coating. This reduces the efficiency below pure copper, depending on the thickness of the coating, but it remains above that of a nickel bit.

Iron-coated bits are usually given an outside coating of cadmium to prevent the iron surface rusting. This type of bit has a reasonable efficiency and can be run at considerably higher temperatures than a pure copper bit, but its tip must be kept well tinned with solder to avoid the build-up of a tough oxide coating.

How to Solder

When an iron is first put into service the tip of the bit must be processed. This is simply performed by running the iron up to temperature and applying resin-cored solder to the tip. The whole of the tip will then become coated with solder. This is called tinning. Surplus solder can be wiped off with a piece of thick cloth or felt.

Once tinned, the iron is ready for action and delay should be avoided because an idling iron causes the build-up of a film of oxidisation on the surface of the solder, and it is undesirable to transfer this to the jointing metals since it can impair the efficiency of the electrical connection.

However, if it is required that the iron remains hot, yet out of action, for some time, a large blob of solder should be applied to the tip, since the surface of this will oxidise instead of the metal tip of the iron itself. Since the latest irons run up to working temperatures quite quickly, it is best to disconnect the iron from the supply during any protracted period of disuse.

When an iron has been idling, the oxidisation developed on the tinning must be removed with a wiping cloth and new solder applied to the tip before the iron is used. This brings us to the stage of making the soldered joint. The idea is to apply the tip, laden with the newly applied fluxed solder, to the joint, holding it in firm contact while the temperature of the joint metals rises sufficiently themselves to melt solder.

At this juncture the end of the resin-cored solder is applied to the joint—*not* to the tip of the bit—with the tip remaining in contact with the joint metals until the molten solder is evenly distributed in and around the joint. It is important for the heat to be applied long enough to secure an even flow of solder, but prolonged application is undesirable because it allows the heat from the iron to be conducted to the adjacent components through the leadout wires and printed circuit conductors. Even if this does not ruin the components alto-

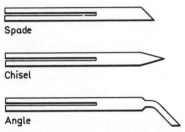

Fig. 5.8   The three most poular types of bit.

gether, it can alter their values and characteristics, especially when small resistors, capacitors and semiconductors are involved.

A good soldered joint can only be obtained when the metals are perfectly clean, and in this connection it is often desirable to tin the jointing metals before the joint is mechanically processed. That is, to scrape and then tin the ends of the component leadout wires and the tags and so forth to which they are to be connected. Tinning in this context refers simply to applying a thin coating of solder to the metal surfaces with the iron, after which the mechanical joint can be processed (i.e. bending the wire round the tag, etc.) and then finally soldered.

Tinning ensures that a near perfect connection is secured and, as already mentioned, leads, tags, eyelets and the like used in electronics are already tinned or plated to facilitate soldering. Older components, however, or those which have been stored for some time might well need retinning.

If a lot of tinning is to be undertaken it is possible to fit a small 'soldering pot' to the end of the iron containing molten solder, the wires are then dipped into this for tinning. Some irons are specially designed to accommodate soldering pots of this kind.

Using a Heat Shunt

When soldering delicate components like transistors, integrated circuits and semiconductor diodes it is extremely important to make sure that heat conduction to the components from the iron through the leadout wires is minimal.

This can be achieved by (a) using an iron whose bit runs sufficiently hot to melt the solder quickly, thereby minimising the time of contact between the bit and the joint metals, (b) pretinning the joint metals to accelerate the soldering process, as mentioned earlier and (c) employing a heat shunt on the component leadout wire being soldered. A heat shunt is nothing more than a metal mass clipped on to the leadout wire, but it must be in good thermal contact with the wire to block the heat conduction, so to speak, and to prevent it rising through the wire to the component.

In the Antex soldering kit (see Fig. 5.6) the heat shunt consists of a pair of flat-ended, spring-closed tweezers. These are clipped on to the wire leadout and remain in position under their own spring pressure, thereby allowing both hands to be used for soldering. A pair of pointed nose pliers can be used similarly, but these are not so convenient to use since they have to be held in pressure on to the

Fig. 5.9   The desoldering gun, marketed by AB Engineering Company, in action.

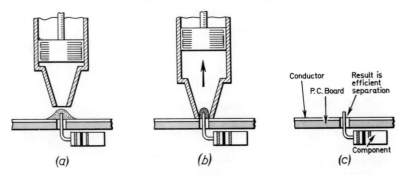

Fig. 5.10   Showing the three phases of action in the AB Engineering desoldering gun. These are explained in the text.

wire. A good heat shunt can be made by winding silver paper or tin-foil round the jaws of a crocodile clip and clipping this on to the wire.

Desoldering Tools

During the course of servicing printed circuit equipment the need frequently arises for the removal of a defective component or a suspect component so that a known good replacement can be tried. When the component to be removed is known to be faulty, then it does not matter very much if it is destroyed during the process of extraction, but there are times when destruction for removal can affect adjacent components and, of course, times when the component might not be faulty. In these instances a more scientific approach is desirable, and this is aided by a recent generation of tools designed specifically for desoldering.

One such tool of this kind is shown in Fig. 5.9. This is called a de-soldering *gun*, and is marketed by *AB Engineering Company* of Watford. It is a hand-operated device which works by suction, as shown in Fig. 5.10. First the gun is loaded by depressing the plunger which automatically locks in the 'ready' position (a). The nozzle, made of tough PTFE (heat-resistant plastics), is then placed in position over the joint in which the solder is melted by the use of an ordinary soldering iron, and the plunger is released by activating a lever conveniently situated on the body.

This results in a strong suction which extracts the molten solder from the joint by drawing it up into the gun, where it solidifies (b). When the plunger is depressed again the small pellets of hardened solder are ejected. The total removal of the solder from the joint in this manner thus allows the speedy extraction of an incorrectly-positioned or malfunctioning component (c).

This kind of gun is ideal for printed circuit board applications, and it has the advantage that it can be operated successfully with one hand only, leaving the other hand to guide the soldering iron, as shown in Fig. 5.9. The design includes a safety shield surrounding the plunger, and allows for the easy replacement of a worn PTFE nozzle.

A desoldering *tool* of a different kind is shown in Fig. 5.11. This is the *Adamin* by *Light Soldering Developments Limited* of Croydon, which uses a stiff rubber bulb for providing the suction, and also a heating element for melting the solder in the joint.

A similar arrangement by *Adcola Products Limited* is shown in Fig. 5.12. The working end of this, however, resembles more of a soldering bit. In fact, the device can be used for soldering—having interchangeable bits—as well as desoldering, which is useful. The solder is sucked through a hole in the bit when the rubber bulb is released and can be later removed from a cavity at the base of the bit. This works very well indeed.

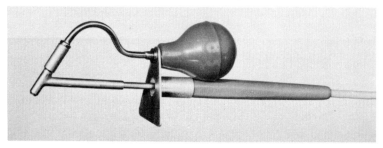

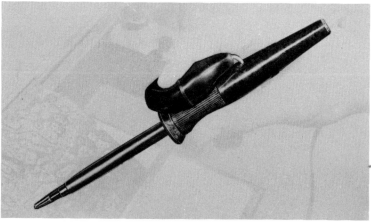

A desoldering tool which requires either an air-line or an ordinary foot pump for operation is shown in Fig. 5.13. This is an *Antex* product which, at the working end of the tool, creates a suction by means of the 'Venturi' principle from compressed air. Owing to the through flow of pressurised air, the tool continually cleans itself and blockages due to residual flux and dirt particles are avoided. The tool also provides its own heating bit, while the molten solder is caught and hardened in a stainless steel catcher.

There are two models, one for normal radio and television desoldering work and the other more suitable for miniature and microminiature applications, such as modules used in computers, hearing aids and so forth. The first is equipped with a 4mm bit and the second with a 2.4mm bit. The action of the device can be understood better by reference to Fig. 5.14.

Other Soldering Aids

As soldering irons run at high temperatures they can prove rather dangerous to person and equipment if incorrectly housed or

Fig. 5.11 (left, top) The Adamin desoldering tool is self-heated and uses a rubber bulb to generate the suction.

Fig. 5.12 (left, bottom) The Adcola desoldering tool is also self-heated and rubber bulb operated.

Fig. 5.13 (right) This type of desoldering tool by Antex requires either an air pressure line or a foot pump to produce the suction by a Venturi action.

positioned when idling. The iron should always be equipped with a stand of some kind, and a wide variety of these are available from the soldering iron firms. A couple of examples from the *Antex* firm are shown in Figs. 5.15 and 5.16.

The first is a fairly straightforward stand designed to accommodate the iron neatly, while the second is designed for either vertical (on a bench, shelf, etc.) or horizontal (on a wall) mounting, and has screw-fixing facilities and also a position at the rear for a large reel of resin-cored solder. Fig. 5.17 shows a protective shield from the *Adcola* range.

Other soldering aids include heat shunts, wire strippers, wire cutters and so forth, many of which have no specific connection with printed circuit applications.

Some of the small irons incorporate a hook on their handles, but this must never be used indiscriminately for parking the iron, say, on the chassis of a radio set or on the arm of a bench light. Not only is this action likely to result in the hot bit pointing dangerously into the face of the operator, but it can also encourage short-circuits, especially when the iron is earthed (as it should be) and the chassis of the set is 'live'! Indiscriminate parking invariably leads to burnt cloths and to charred insulation along the power cables, to say nothing of personal danger. These troubles are completely avoided when the iron is placed properly into a holder, stand or protection shield.

Soldering Precautions

If the metal parts of the iron are incorrectly earthed it is possible for small transient currents to flow from the mains supply via the element insulation of the iron and into transistorised circuitry by way of the bit. This is not uncommonly responsible for failures in transistors, integrated circuits and semiconductor diodes.

The iron, then, for this reason if not for reasons of safety, should

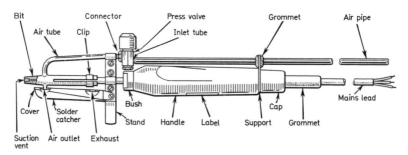

Fig. 5.15 (top, left) Antex soldering iron standard designed for wall or bench fitting with position for reel of solder.

Fig. 5.16 (top, right) A simple soldering iron stand by Antex.

Fig. 5.17 (right) Soldering iron shield manufactured by Adcola.

Fig. 5.14 (left) showing the component parts of the Antex desoldering tool.

always be connected to the earth pin on the mains plug. This is the green and yellow wire—with the brown being 'live' and the blue 'neutral'—but this should always be checked for wiring might correspond to the earlier colour code, now obsolete.

When a low voltage iron is used from the mains supply a step-down transformer is essential, of course, but this should be of the isolated winding type—never an auto-transformer, for this will *not* isolate the iron element from the full mains potential. When soldering with the miniature and sub-miniature type of iron the power lead must never be held in the palm of the hand or bent at an angle where it protrudes from the handle. This incorrect way of handling a soldering iron is avoided by holding the iron as a pencil is held, between the first finger and the thumb.

Soldering Guns

Also becoming very popular is the soldering gun. There are various types, but with all the name describes the styling. Fig. 5.18 shows the Ersa *Sprint*, marketed by Home Radio (Components) Ltd., of 234–240 London Road, Mitcham, Surrey, CR4 3HD.

This is a very light-weight soldering tool, which is easily handled, as shown in Fig. 5.18. A switch at the trigger position energises the element, which is mains powered (direct, not needing a transformer) and the design is such that full soldering power is available within the short time period of about ten seconds. This can be very useful (I, personally, have found it so) when only periodic soldering is required during a servicing operation, for example.

Temperature can be controlled merely by releasing the trigger switch when the bit gets too hot and applying pressure again when it cools off. Quite a high working temperature can be obtained for large joints. It is possible to solder together up to eight 1·5 square mm. conductors, which gives some idea of the heat capacity. Design is for soldering bit interchange, and a selection of bits—copper and nickel plated—are available for various applications.

Another gun iron is shown in Fig. 5.19. This, by Klaus Schlitt of D6 Frankfurt/Main 61, Konstanzer Str. 73, is designed for 'one-handed soldering', leaving the other hand free to manipulate the workpieces. Automatic feed of soldering wire to the tip of the bit makes this possible, and the general mechanics of the instrument are shown in Fig. 5.20.

The solder on a reel is located at the handle end and arrives at the tip through a special feed and transport system which is operated by pressing the push-button. The amount of solder passed to the tip

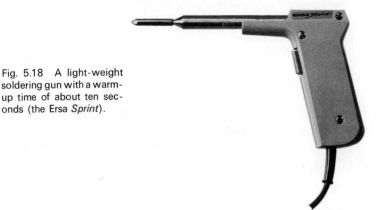

Fig. 5.18 A light-weight soldering gun with a warm-up time of about ten seconds (the Ersa *Sprint*).

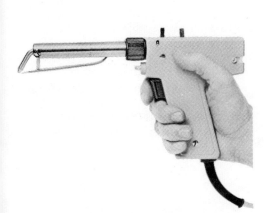

Fig. 5.19 Soldering gun with automatic solder feed, permitting one handed soldering (Klaus Schlitt).

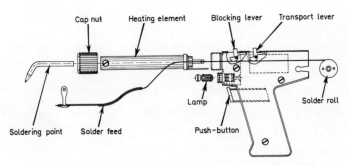

Fig. 5.20 Mechanical details of the gun shown in Fig. 5.19.

can be increased by pressing the push-button several times. Models are available for 110V, 220V (suitable also for 240V) and 24V.

The first two models incorporate the built-in illumination, shown in Fig. 5.20. Weight is 8oz. (230 grams) and wattages 20, 30, 40, 50 and 60 for the higher voltage models and 20, 30 and 40W for the 24V model (which can be obtained from a mains transformer). Accessories include a range of soldering bits, plug-in holder for solder reels, mains transformer for the low-voltage model and bench stand.

Desoldering Braid

I have already detailed various types of desoldering instruments based on a 'sucking' action. There is another which does not need air lines or any pumping, called the Litesold Desoldering Tool. A different scheme which enlists capillary attraction for the desoldering effect is marketed by Solderstat Ltd., manufacturers of a wide advanced range of Elremco Wolf soldering equipment.

This is called *Desoldering Braid* (Fig. 5.21). The idea is to apply the braid to the soldered joint along with the soldering iron, and when the solder melts it is absorbed into the mesh of the braid by capillary attraction. Fig. 5.24 shows such tape being used during a servicing operation on a modern printed circuit board. This is compared with a similar 'action' photograph of desoldering in Fig. 5.22, using the Adcola tool already mentioned.

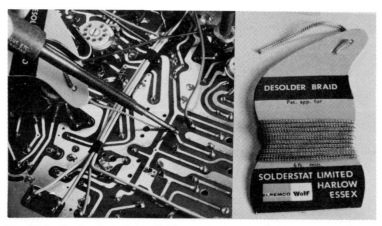

Fig. 5.21 Application of the *Solderstat* desoldering braid, which works on capillary attraction, and (right) the desoldering braid on dispenser.

Fig. 5.22   A desoldering exercise using the Adcola tool with rubber bulb.

Desoldering Heads

Later in this chapter (under Replacing Components, page 111) hints are given for the extraction of soldered-in printed circuits and of multi-terminal components, such as i.f. transformers. Under some conditions this protracted procedure is necessary, which is why it has been mentioned. However, the various desoldering devices can remove a great deal of toil from such operations with far less risk to adjacent components and wiring.

To help with the speedy removal of multi-terminal devices, such as ICs, a number of manufacturers have developed special desoldering heads or blocks which are fitted on to the hot shank of a soldering iron in place of the ordinary bit. One firm specialising in this hardware is Weller Electric Ltd., which is also noted for a wide range of soldering equipment.

Blocks from this firm are available for the desoldering of dual in-line packages of 14 and 16 leads. Also available are reflow soldering tips for dual in-line packages and for flat packs, Fig. 5.23 showing the flat pack tip by the side of the corresponding device. These allow immediate solder reflow over the multiple joints when a replacement device is fitted.

Solderstat Ltd. (Elremco Wolf) is another firm handling IC

desoldering heads, suitable models being available for 14-way and 16-way devices. Fitment is to the standard HMS Miniature Soldering Iron made by the firm. The heads are machined in one piece to secure good thermal conduction and long life, while the accurately dimensioned slots on the active face permit easy location on the work piece, even where access is difficult.

One of the smaller Elremco Wolf soldering instruments (similar to the HMS just mentioned, but for lighter applications) is shown in action in Fig. 5.24. This is a type MS, 240V, 10W model.

Temperature Control

Soldering tools with automatic temperature control are gaining popularity. Temperature control means that the operating warm-up time is decreased because of the use of a more powerful heating element, the current being switched off automatically when the required soldering temperature is reached.

Irons without heat control continue to increase in temperature until the heat produced by the element is balanced by the loss due to radiation or conduction into the work pieces. Thus, if an uncontrolled iron has been idling for some time its bit temperature could rise significantly above that required for a soldering task. This may be too great for the work pieces, solder and flux.

Temperature-controlled irons embody some kind of heat sensing device close to the working point of the soldering bit. The temperature controlled irons by Weller Electric Ltd., for example, use bits in which the sensing device is an integral part; control at different temperatures thus being achieved merely by changing the tip, using the same wattage iron.

The curves in Fig. 5.25(a)—by Weller—show the different warm-up and control characteristics of several irons relative to an iron using a temperatured-controlled tip. This brings out the more rapid warm-up time of a controlled iron and reveals that the heat reserve provides adequate margin for heat loss through the work pieces coupled with fast temperature recovery at the conclusion of a soldering exercise.

The diagram in Fig. 5.25(b), also by Weller, reveals the difference between a Weller temperature-controlled iron and an uncontrolled iron working under conditions of continuous jointing. Here it will be seen that the controlled iron remains stable, with speedy temperature recovery between each operation, compared with the initially greater temperature of an uncontrolled iron, but which progressively falls to the soldering threshold temperature with increasing number of soldering cycles.

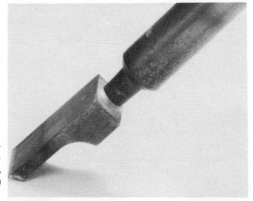

Fig. 5.23 Reflow solder-
ing tip for dual in-line and
flat packs (Weller Electric).

Fig. 5.24 (below) Minia-
ture Elremco Wolf solder-
ing instrument in action,
Model MS (240V, 10W)
from Solderstat.

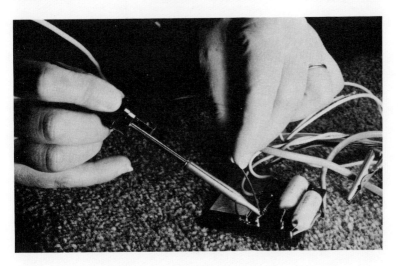

In addition to these factors, of course, temperature control reduces tip wear rate, which is commonly high during idling periods of uncontrolled irons due to the progressive rise in temperature.

Methods of Control

The *modus operandi* of the Weller temperature control is illustrated in Fig. 5.25(c). The permanent magnet is attracted to the temperature sensing element when the tip is cold. This pulls on the power supply switch. As the tip temperature rises the sensing element releases the magnet, which then retracts and pushes the switch off. When the

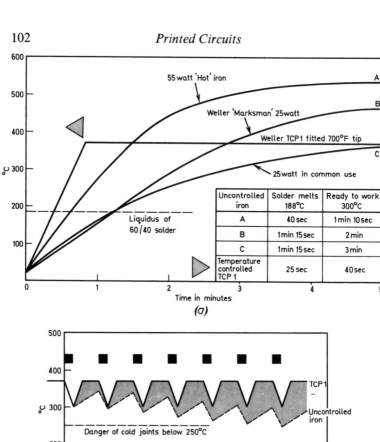

	Uncontrolled iron	Solder melts 188°C	Ready to work 300°C
A		40 sec	1 min 10 sec
B		1 min 15 sec	2 min
C		1 min 15 sec	3 min
Temperature controlled TCP 1		25 sec	40 sec

(a)

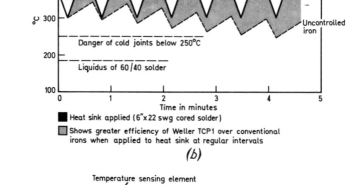

■ Heat sink applied (6"x22 swg cored solder)

▨ Shows greater efficiency of Weller TCP1 over conventional irons when applied to heat sink at regular intervals

(b)

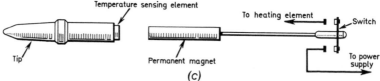

(c)

Fig. 5.25 Temperature control. (a) heating-up times, tip temperatures measured in free air at 20 deg. C; (b) recovery from repeated thermal loads for 10 sec. followed by 30 sec. recovery; (c) Curie point temperature sensing principle (Weller Electric).

tip temperature falls slightly, as during a soldering exercise, the sensing element again attracts the magnet to resume heating.

The magnetic attraction effect described is based on the Curie point principle, the action thus occurring at the tip Curie point, since the field strength of a magnet is affected by temperature. The Weller desoldering tool, using a press-bulb for the 'sucking' action, also has built-in temperature control. This tool is shown in Fig. 5.26 in a complementary stand.

Fig. 5.26   Desoldering tool with temperature control (Weller Electric).

Other firms, of course, make temperature-controlled soldering tools, some based on simple bi-metal strip control. That by Solderstat, however, employs a solid-state temperature sensor located close to the working point of the soldering bit. This feeds a 'signal', based on the thermal conditions at the tip, to a solid-state controller which maintains the required temperature of the bit within close limits and automatically compensates for the thermal loads imposed by the work pieces as well as for fluctuations in mains supply voltage.

This iron is complete with stand, and a control dial on this allows ready adjustment to the controlled temperature. The iron used in this partnership is similar to the MS and HMS series already referred to.

There are also irons complete with stand whose idling temperature is reduced when the iron is placed in the stand, this action diminishing the power fed to the heating element. It is obviously impossible to investigate all the excellent irons and soldering tools currently available or, indeed, to mention all the manufacturers producing them; but it is hoped that the items which have been mentioned will give the reader some idea of the vastness of the range and of the specialised techniques which have been evolved to optimise two of the most important aspects of electronics—those of soldering and desoldering.

Fluxes and PCB Coatings

These days we do not have to worry much about flux for we usually find it as a core in cored solder. However, a word or two about this important soldering material will not be amiss. Flux is necessary to dissolve tarnish on the surfaces of the jointing metals and to seal them from contact with the air right through to the conclusion of the soldering operation (also see page 81).

Moreover, the flux should not encourage corrosion and, if necessary, it should be of a nature for easy removal from the metal surfaces after soldering; it should be effectively 'dissolved' by the molten solder and promote the easy flow of the solder over the joint by reducing the surface-tension effect of the molten solder.

Early fluxes were organic and inorganic based, including 'killed' (inert) acids and water soluble crystals. These are still used in some applications, but the electronic industry mostly favours essentially non-corrosive fluxes with a resin base (sometimes called rosin or colophony). This is basically the gum which is yielded by the bark of pine trees when cut (obtained in a similar way to pure rubber). Water-white resin is chemically inert, even when heated, and possesses relatively good wetting and spreading properties. Such a flux is often used for delicate instrument work.

However, for the soldering of tarnished surfaces, such as often found in general electronics, basic resin flux is insufficiently potent for good and easy soldering, and to make it more suitable for this sort of jointing an activator, such as hydrazine, hydrochloride or glutamic acid hydrochloride, is incorporated. It is then called 'activated resin flux'. This is the type often found in cored solder and is essentially free from corrosive effects provided that it is heated for sufficient time to conclude the decomposition of the activator. This problem, though, is solved when the flux consists of a core running through the solder wire.

Printed circuit boards are sometimes coated with a protection consisting of a resin-based flux material. This facilitates the unsoldering and soldering of circuit and component conductors. There are also other kinds of protective coatings, examples being Vycoat ACA60 and CA90, the former in 14oz (35 grams) aerosol tins and the latter in bulk of 1 or 5gal. It is self-based and air dries and cures in normal ambient temperatures.

Oxidation and degradation of printed circuit board conductors is prevented by the coating, and the nature of the material allows repairs to be carried out by soldering through the coating, the affected area being restored afterwards by a quick respray from the aerosol tin. The film should be applied in two stages to a thickness of about 100µm. Insulation rating is 3kV.

Servicing Aspects

It is often possible to fault diagnose in printed circuit equipment without removing the board from the chassis. Many items of equipment, especially that of the more complex class, like computers, colour television sets and the more involved radios and hi-fi equipment, contain tests points terminated to parts of the circuit on which exist important working voltages.

Thus, by connecting the negative side of the test meter, say to the chassis or 'earthy' side of the circuit, the positive voltages in the various parts of the circuit of a defective item of equipment can be quickly checked against the correct voltages given in the service manual or service chart with little more fuss than evoked by the removal of the cover.

It is a good idea to check as many voltages in and around the circuit without making too many disconnections and reconnections which, under some conditions, can temporarily correct a fault condition, especially when it is of an intermittent kind. If test points are not fitted, then it is not generally difficult to seek out certain vantage test points on inter-connecting wires and terminals, valveholder tags, transformer tags and control tags.

In-Situ Diagnosis

Owing to the problems involved in removing components for substitution tests and in their possible subsequent refitting, as much information as possible on how the circuit is operating should be gleaned by using a more scientific approach to fault diagnosis. We shall see later that there is an instrument designed specifically to test transistors and diodes actually in circuit, thereby avoiding the need for unsoldering and possibly resoldering this somewhat vulnerable class of component.

However, with the basic test equipment we can discover quite a bit about the working of a circuit by checking the voltages and monitoring the currents in terms of voltages across resistive elements in the circuit with the least amount of physical disturbance.

Let us suppose, for instance, that the initial tests have indicated that the audio section of a receiver is defunct, and that we have a suspicion that the driver stage is for some reason inactive (see Fig. 5.27). A logical first move, therefore, would be to discover whether or not the driver stage is working correctly from the d.c. point of view.

If we have already found out that voltage (negative, in this case, with respect to chassis) is present at, say, the top of the collector load resistor (R_c) in Fig. 5.27, then we can of course, check continuity of R_c by dropping the negative probe of the meter to the collector of the transistor. Current in R_c will make the voltage here less than that at the top of the resistor.

This is all very well, but we might wish to check the collector current. One way of doing this to to disconnect the resistor at the negative voltage line or the collector itself and introduce a milli-ammeter. This is not a good way, as we have seen; a better way is to connect a low-reading voltmeter across R_c, as shown by *Test 1*. If current is flowing, then a voltage will be developed across the resistor of a value depending on the current and the value of the resistor.

By using Ohm's law and knowing the value of R_c we can easily find the current in milliamperes by dividing the voltage reading by the value of the resistor in thousands of ohms. Let us suppose that we read just 6 volts on the meter and that the resistor has a value of $2,000\Omega$, then 6 divided by 2 equals 3, which is the number of mA of collector current.

This sort of thing can be practised almost anywhere in the circuit where current is passing through a known value resistor. *Test 2* in Fig. 5.27 shows the idea extended to the emitter circuit. The voltage across the emitter resistor R_e this time being measured. This test is less accurate unless a very low reading voltmeter is available, owing to the usually low value of R_e.

If we accurately compute the collector current and the emitter current as just shown, we shall find that the latter is a shade higher than the former. This is because R_e passes not only the collector current but also the forward current in the emitter/base junction of the transistor. If there is neither collector current nor emitter current, yet the collector voltage is present, either the transistor is defective or the base circuit is incorrectly biased.

It is difficult to check base current accurately *in-situ* because it is normally very small, often the matter of microamperes. In Fig. 5.27 the base is biased from the potential-divider across the supply given by R1 and R2, this making the base just a little negative with respect to the emitter (note that this is so with p-n-p transistors, as that in Fig. 5.27, but that all the polarities are reversed with n-p-n transistors).

If R1 increases significantly in value or goes open-circuit, then the base bias would be either small or non-existent, and in either case the collector (and emitter) current would be very small or zero (even with zero base bias there may be some current in the collector circuit due to collector leakage, and this rises with increase in temperature of the transistor).

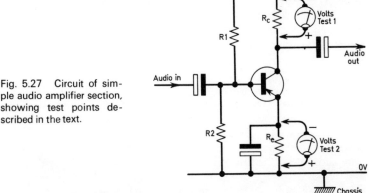

Fig. 5.27 Circuit of simple audio amplifier section, showing test points described in the text.

Conversely, if R2 goes high or open-circuit, the base current will increase and the collector current will rise to an abnormally high value. It is possible under this condition for the transistor to 'bottom', meaning the inability of the transistor to yield further collector current by an increase in base bias. These sort of considerations, however, apply more to general servicing, and they are fully dealt with in books on transistor techniques and servicing.

For the sake of completeness, though, it is noteworthy that faulty biasing can be diagnosed without upsetting the printed circuit board too much by connecting a voltmeter as in *Test 1* and then shunting either R1 or R2 with a resistor several times the value of that which it is shunting, while observing the voltage reading.

If there is no reading to start with, but collector current is indicated when, say, R1 is shunted, then the biasing is faulty (not the transistor). This could be the result of an open-circuit R1, for instance. On the other hand, if the starting current is abnormally high, dropping to a more reasonable value when R2 is shunted, the significance is excessive bias, and R2 should then be checked for open-circuit or value increase.

Technicians fully conversant with the art of servicing transistored circuits often adopt such artifices for accelerating fault finding, and in some cases it is possible to use the resistance existing across the test prods of a voltmeter for shunting tests of the kind just explained. It is essential, of course, to know the value of the resistance appearing across the test prods over the various voltage ranges, but this is not difficult to work out when the ohms-per-volt sensitivity of the instrument is known.

A testmeter with a sensitivity of 20,000Ω/volt has 20,000Ω across the prods for every full-scale volt. Thus, if the meter is switched, say, to 100 volts (that is full-scale), then the resistance is 100 times 20,000Ω, or 2MΩ. Switched to the 10-volt range, the resistance would be 200,000Ω, and so on. Care must be exercised in avoiding circuits on which the voltage is in excess of that to which the meter is switched.

In-Circuit Testing

Fig. 5.28 shows an instrument designed for testing transistors and diodes while in circuit on a printed circuit board. This is called the 'Diotestor', made by *Britec Limited* of Charing Cross Road, London WC2. It is essentially a 'go–no-go' tester which checks the conduction and cut-off conditions of transistors (both p-n-p and n-p-n) and diodes without the need for unsoldering. The device is composed of three sections: a rear battery holder; a central housing incorporating the electronic test circuit, an indicator light and selector switches. There is also a stainless-steel probe assembly consisting of three spring-loaded pins to TO-5 transistor spacing.

The tester is worked by first switching it to n-p-n or p-n-p to suit the transistor under test and then pressing the three probes against the appropriate transistor leadout terminations on the printed side of the board. The board must, of course, be disconnected from the power source, and under this condition the transistor will be cut-off (non-conducting). This condition is signified by the indicator lamp on the tester failing to light.

If the lamp is lit, however, a short-circuit between the emitter and collector of the transistor is indicated. Assuming that the lamp is unlit, the transistor can be caused to conduct by pressing a button on the tester, and if all is well with the transistor the indicator lamp will light. Should the lamp extinguish when the button is pressed, then the transistor most likely has a short-circuit between the emitter and base.

There is a limit to the amount of circuit resistance that can be catered for in these tests, however, and for mounted transistors the

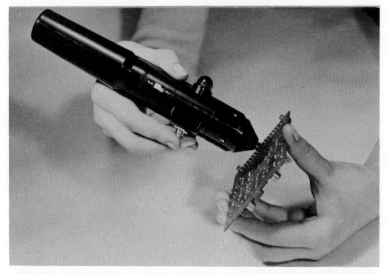

Fig. 5.28   The *Diotestor* for *in situ* tests of transistors and semi-conductor diodes.

external resistance of the emitter/base circuit must exceed 1,000Ω for silicon transistors and 600Ω for germanium transistors (these values allow for low amplification transistors, but general testing is possible with even lower resistance values). The total in-circuit resistance of the emitter/collector and base/collector circuits (taken as being in parallel) must also exceed 1,000Ω.

Unmounted transistors can also be tested and, then, of course, the in-circuit resistance limits do not apply. An extension lead terminated with a socket at one end for accepting the probe pins and at the other with clips for connecting to the transistor leadout wires is available for this purpose.

This extension lead can also be used for testing unmounted diodes, but for the testing of mounted diodes an adaptor with adjustable pin settings—to suit the leadout termination distance between the 'anode' and 'cathode' of the diode under test—is available, the design of which accepts the three probes of the tester. The diode-testing adaptor pins are simply pressed against the in-circuit diode under test and the n-p-n–p-n-p switch on the tester alternated from one position to the other. If this action results in the indicator lamp switching on and off, then the diode is in good condition.

Breaks in Printed Circuits

Probably one of the biggest causes of trouble in the smaller, domestic type of printed circuit equipment is fracture of one or more of the printed conductors of the circuit. This not uncommonly happens when a small transistor radio set, for example, is dropped.

There is either a degree of intermittency—the set cutting on or off when pressure is applied to the printed circuit board—or the set is completely dead. This sort of trouble usually requires the normal servicing techniques to establish the area in which the fault exists, especially when the set remains dead.

In the event of the set restoring to normal working when pressure is applied to the printed circuit board it is sometimes possible to locate the circuit break by applying controlled pressure in and around the printed circuit board. It is necessary to do this with the set running, of course, and while personal damage from electric shock is unlikely with battery-powered equipment, extreme care must be taken when the equipment is mains-powered.

It is a good idea to make or acquire a non-metallic tool for probing around the circuit. A plastics knitting needle is suitable. The scheme is to use the tool for pressing along the lines of the circuit, not too hard but just hard enough to get the board to flex locally where the pressure is applied.

With a bit of luck the point of conductor break can be located by the set coming to life when a very small pressure is applied to the area in which the trouble exists. As many causes of this trouble result from hair-line cracks in the conductors, a magnifying glass is useful for scrutinising the conductors within the established fault area.

When the break has been located it can be easily repaired with a small blob of solder, taking care not to overheat the circuit board unduly as this could impair the adhesion of the copper strips and give rise to further trouble later on. If the actual point of fracture cannot be isolated, it sometimes pays to cut away the whole of the suspect conductor and remake the circuit with a wire link or by the use of *Cir-Kit* (see Chapter 4).

Of course, it is easily possible to prove that a break exists in a printed conductor by means of an ohmmeter, but when the test prods of such an instrument are applied to the circuit good continuity may be inhibited by the protective lacquer coating of the conductors.

It is essential, therefore, to remove this lacquer from the points where the prods are to be connected, and this can be done with an acetone fluid or similar solvent. If considerable printed circuit board servicing is contemplated, it might pay to make up a special set of test prods with fine, sharp points which can be pressed through the lacquer into good contact with the metal strips.

Sometimes it is possible to detect a conductor break on translucent laminate by arranging for a bench light to illuminate one side of the board, while the circuit conductors are scrutinised on the other side. Again, a magnifying glass is a useful aid in detecting hair-line breaks.

Replacing Components

Earlier in this chapter is was explained how a desoldering tool can facilitate the replacement of individual components mounted on printed circuit boards. Wherever possible this method should be practised, but there are times when a different technique is warranted, especially when for some reason or other it is not required to remove the board from the equipment.

For example, small components, like resistors and capacitors, can be replaced by (a) cutting the faulty component with snips or crushing with pliers, (b) cutting the old component from its leadout wires, leaving as much wire as possible at each side for connecting to the replacement component, (c) forming the ends of the leadout wires of the old component—still attached to the board—into small loops, (d) threading the leadout wires of the new component through the loops, bending round to provide good mechanical terminations and cutting off surplus wire and (e) finally soldering.

To replace other components, like i.f. transformers, switches, control potentiometers and valveholders, it is often necessary to remove the printed circuit board from the main chassis assembly. This must be performed with great care, for undue flexing of the board or, indeed, any rough treatment, can fracture the printed conductors and give rise to a great deal of extra trouble.

All the interconnecting and main connecting wires should be removed from the board, either by unplugging, unwinding or unsoldering, depending on the precise design; then, if the board is fixed to the metal chassis by soldering to lugs, heat from a soldering iron should be directed first to one fixing point until the solder is melted.

At this stage the board should be very carefully lifted at that one point until it rises no more than about an eighth of an inch. The solder should then be allowed to harden. The same procedure should then be adopted at each fixing point in turn, working round all the fixing points, until the board is eventually removed from all anchor points. This scheme avoids excessive bending of the board, which would be necessary if each point was unsoldered and the board lifted completely clear in one action.

The idea, then, is to lift the board from each fixing point a little at a time, working round all the fixings as many times as required to release the board completely without stress. Fortunately, many boards are either screwed or clipped into position, so this rather protracted method of board removal is not always necessary. Moreover, the desoldering aids already considered can significantly ease this sort of operation.

When working on a printed circuit board that has been extracted from a chassis assembly it is desirable to improvise some sort of support by wooden blocks of sufficient depth to accommodate the height of coils, i.f. cans, tuning capacitors and so forth. Alternatively a proper printed circuit frame can be utilised. These are adjustable to cater for any normal size of board and contain a swivel to allow the board to be easily orientated to any convenient working position.

I.F. transformers can be extracted by applying just enough heat to the terminations and screening can supports to melt the solder, thereby allowing the component to be levered clear of the copper strips. Before replacing a component of this kind, however, the fixing and termination holes should be cleared of solder either by the use of a desoldering gun or by shaking out the blocking solder immediately after removing the soldering iron.

Other components with tag terminations and fixing lugs should be removed in a similar way, and when resoldering the use of excessive solder should be avoided. The original tinning of the component lugs, terminations and board conductors will make soldering easy, and under this condition more solder than really necessary can inadvertently be applied, sometimes causing it to run between conductors on the board and join them. Look out for this.

When replacing components with leadout wires, the wires should not be pulled tight between the fixing holes or tags, for when the component cools after soldering contraction of the wire can withdraw it from within the component and produce very difficult to locate fault symptoms.

CHAPTER SIX

THE FUTURE OF PRINTED CIRCUITS

ALTHOUGH THE BASIC NATURE of the printed circuit is unlikely to change very much in the future, the trend is already for the circuit board to carry fewer discrete components and a greater number of circuits in separate encapsulations, called integrated circuits (ICs). Indeed, an IC is itself a microscopically-sized assembly incorporating a complete circuit of transistors, sometimes semiconductor diodes and passive components like resistors, so it is not deviating from the general theme of this book to devote a chapter to this new type of circuit.

ICs are already being employed in vast quantities in equipment like computers which call for multiplicities of active elements. They are also appearing in domestically-based electronic equipment, like colour television sets, hi-fi amplifiers, tuner-amplifiers and even in portable radios.

Some ICs look very much like ordinary transistors, having the same type of encapsulation, but with a greater number of wire leadouts. Others have a somewhat different encapsulation, but all types represent merely the basic circuit, which usually has to be 'tailored' by discrete components to give it the characteristic demanded by the design of the equipment as a whole.

Thus, several ICs may appear on a printed circuit board along with the necessary discrete components to get them to operate in the way intended by the equipment designer. For example, the TAD100 IC used in the Roberts RIC.1 portable radio provides eleven transistors and eleven resistors for the mixer, local oscillator, i.f. strip, detector and first a.f. stages. The other components required to make these stages work as they would in the ordinary structure are provided by separate (discrete) components on the printed circuit board, and these include those components for tuning and so forth.

However, before getting on to hybrid circuits, let us take a more detailed look at the IC as a 'component'. Of course, it is totally impossible in the short compass of this one chapter to delve in any depth into IC theory or, indeed, to consider the large number of IC

113

designs in detail. Nevertheless, we can get a fair idea of the state of the art by considering two forms of IC; one using 'solid' circuits, called solid or 'monolithic', and the other based on the depositing of the circuit and elements in the form of evaporated thin films or printed thick films upon an insulating substrate, called 'thin-film' and 'thick-film' circuits.

Monolithic Devices

Basically, the monolithic IC is a combined multilayer device using two layers of crystal (p- and n-type) to create diode junctions, thereby restricting the current flow from layer to layer in one direction only, and three layers to form the inbuilt transistors, with n-p-n and/or p-n-p characteristics.

As with semiconductor diodes and transistors in discrete form, the characteristics are provided by the nature of the crystals used and the impurities which are introduced into them.

When the various active elements are created in the IC, the same impurities forming them can also be arranged to develop small resistors and sometimes capacitors; the resistors are easy, of course, since they merely constitute point-to-point connections across the circuit elements of impurity governed by the amount of resistance required.

Capacitors are less easy to simulate in terms of the nature of the component in discrete configuration, but the problem is sometimes solved by using diode elements as capacitors, for when semiconductor devices of this kind are reverse-biased they possess a specific value of capacitance across their electrodes, the value decreasing with increase in reverse bias.

The internal connections are developed in a similar manner to the conductors of a printed circuits board, the 'wiring skeleton', however, being of dramatically smaller size than ordinary printed circuit boards. In fact, a fully processed IC is just about visible with the naked eye, although the components and 'wiring' cannot be seen without optical aid.

Of course, the circuit is first drawn and designed at convenient drawing board dimensions; it is then photographed in multiples of the same design and by means of a special reducing camera the designs are 'projected' onto the silicon crystal in such a manner that the unwanted parts of the circuit are subsequently etched away, like printed circuit design.

However, the various layers of the IC are usually processed separately, so that one set of master drawings relates specifically to one layer; other masters being used for the other layers. Each layer is thus developed by etching the diminutive circuit pattern reproduced

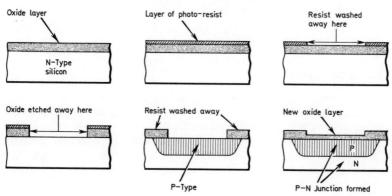

Fig. 6.1   These diagrams show the basic processes involved in the development of an IC.

from the master drawings on to an oxidised surface of the crystal, with special techniques being adopted for the inter-connections of the various layers. Finally, the multiplicity of small ICs is separated into individual circuits and then encapsulated.

N-Type Silicon

The starting point is a single n-type silicon crystal of thickness about 200µm—called a wafer—which is initially coated with a masking layer of silicon dioxide between 0·4 and 0·6µm thick, followed by a layer of photo-resist which is exposed to light through the master negative (as with the printed circuit). The unexposed areas of resist are dissolved away while the remaining areas are hardened, this serving as the etching mask to introduce openings in the silicon dioxide at the appropriate places on the crystal. After etching, the resist is cleaned from the surface, and the zones of p- and n-type semiconductor are processed within the crystal.

This is achieved by a heating action during which time the controlled impurities are added to the crystal. When the zone has been processed, the wafer is again subjected to oxidation, after which further junction zoning can be processed in accordance with the required design configuration. Some idea of the basic processes involved can be gleaned from Fig. 6.1; and it will be appreciated, of course, that contacts are fitted to the various layers to provide the required circuit elements.

Insulation between circuit elements is achieved by the reverse-biasing effect of n-p and p-n junctions. For example, p-type material of the design which is reverse-biased with respect to an adjacent piece of n-type material is effectively 'insulated' from its surroundings, the insulation 'resistance' then being a function of the reverse leakage characteristic of the biased junction.

Capacitors and Resistors

As already mentioned, circuit capacitors are formed by the reverse-biasing of inbuilt diodes, an approach which permits values up to some 200pF to be derived with an accuracy of 3 to 5 per cent. One difficulty, however, is that, since the capacitance depends on the thickness of the diode 'barrier layer', the capacitance decreases with increase in reverse bias potential; further, the impedance of this type of capacitor is not composed purely of capacitive reactance, but of capacitance in combination with parallel and series resistance.

These factors do tend to limit the application of capacitors formed within the circuit, but more critical applications are easily satisfied by the use of external capacitors on the printed circuit board, carrying also other necessary discrete components.

Resistors can be formed between the electrodes of active elements by the resistivity of the p- and n- materials themselves which, of course, are semiconductors, anyway. The resistivity is such that useful values of resistance can be derived from the dimensions of the semiconducting materials existing in the IC makeup. Students of transistors and semiconductors generally will appreciate that for a p-n junction, say, to act as an insulator, the 'resistor' part of the p-type semiconductor must be given a negative potential with respect to the surrounding n-type material.

Diodes

Diodes and capacitors are formed in a manner similar to that illustrated in Fig. 6.1; but there are several complications as shown in Fig. 6.2. Here the connection to the p-type crystal is achieved first by etching an opening into the oxide layer and then by evaporating aluminium on to the exposed surface of the p-type crystal. This demands special skills to avoid the surface of the p-type crystal from being affected by the etching action. In practice, the aluminium is deposited over the whole surface of the semiconductor wafer, after which it is removed, again by etching, from those areas where it is not required.

When the exercise is to create a diode in isolation, then the base of the n-type material is alloyed to a gold-plated underlayer, giving the second termination. In the aspect being considered, however, the diode will form a part of an IC, in which case it usually needs to be

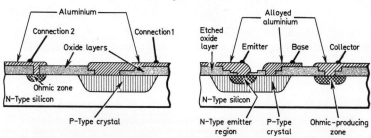

Fig. 6.2 (left) Showing how a diode junction is formed on the IC chip.

Fig. 6.3 (right) Showing how a transistor is formed on an IC chip.

insulated from its surroundings, as in the case of resistors just mentioned.

This means that a connection has to be established in the upper side of the n-type crystal, which brings in another complication based on the fact that aluminium (for the contact) gives rise to a diode action when it is deposited on to n-type crystal. This is a factor that would endow the connection with a high resistance to current passing in one direction and a low resistance to current passing in the opposite direction—in other words, a non-ohmic connection. This is combated by establishing a zone for the connection that possesses characteristics for neutralising the diode effect, as revealed in Fig. 6.2.

Transistors

Fig. 6.3 shows how a transistor is developed into the circuit. Here the basic crystal is n-type, originally with an oxide layer on the top surface, into one end of which is introduced a layer of p-type material by the processes used for creating the diode junction in Fig. 6.1. However, the transistor requires a second junction, and this is formed by the introduction of a layer of n-type material into the layer of p-type material which has previously been introduced into the basic n-type crystal.

This gives the n-type emitter, with the basic crystal wafer acting as the collector and the p-type material as the base, in a transistor of n-p-n type. There are a number of points of detail involved in the formation of a transistor along these lines. The n-type emitter, for example, must contain more donors than acceptors in the base to yield the correct emitter-junction requirement.

Also, when the transistor is a part of an IC, the connection to the collector is made through a termination similar to that shown for the diode in Fig. 6.2, so as to neutralise the non-ohmic effect of alloying aluminium direct to the n-type collector. It will be seen, too, that the connections to the emitter, base and collector are again made by etching openings into the oxide layer and depositing aluminium.

Silicon Chip

As already mentioned, large numbers of circuits are made simultaneously on a single wafer of silicon; indeed, hundreds of circuits of the same kind can be produced on a wafer a mere 2·5cm diameter ! The circuit is generally drawn as a 200 times enlargement, consisting of 'masks' to be employed in all successive operations. The drawings are photographically reduced in two stages, and the final mask is made by repeating the last-reduced master drawing many times on a single negative. As will be appreciated, the working tolerances are very small indeed, and the maximum permissible deviation is about 1μm.

Fig. 6.4 is a microphotograph of a very high speed switching IC based on silicon, and gives a very good idea of what a completed monolithic IC 'chip'—as the substrate is often called—looks like under a microscope. A dramatic illustration of the smallness of an IC chip is shown in Fig. 6.5. This is a complete electronic counting

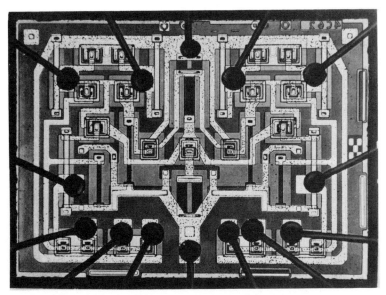

Fig. 6.4   Microphoto of a very high speed silicon IC (Mullard).

circuit by Mullard and of the kind used by the thousands in modern computers. The IC is fabricated on a chip of silicon measuring only 1·5 by 3mm and yet embodies over 120 components.

If the circuit were made with ordinary discrete components, it would occupy a circuit board about 9in. (22·8cm) square—more than one thousand times the size of the silicon chip. The extent of

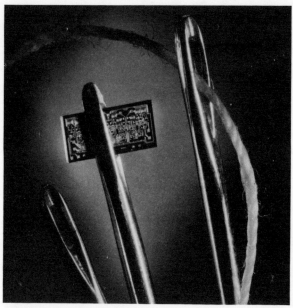

Fig. 6.5   Some idea of the smallness of an IC chip can be appreciated from this photo. Here the sewing needle is an ordinary No. 5, while the cotton—looking like rope!. .is ordinary 40 gauge.

miniaturisation can be appreciated when it is realised that the 'rope' passing through the eye of the magnified sewing needle is merely No. 40 gauge sewing cotton, and that the needle itself is just a No. 5!

Of course, the IC is rarely—if ever—sold in the form shown in Figs. 6.4 and 6.5. Its method of mounting depends on the nature of the equipment in which it is to be used. A popular mounting method involves a standard TO-5 transistor encapsulation, as shown in Fig. 6.6. Here is depicted three monolithic ICs by the side of an ordinary MOS transistor, all by Mullard and mounted on TO-5 heads prior to total encapsulation. Other methods are shown in Fig. 6.7, where (a) shows the dual-in-line encapsulation (see Chapter 4), (b) the

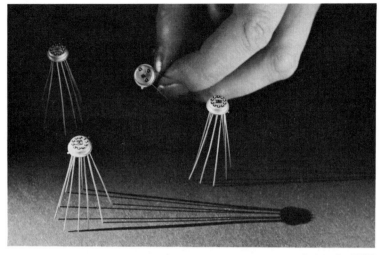

Fig. 6.6   Mullard IC chips fixed on their bases prior to encapsulation. An MOS transistor is also shown for comparison.

'flat-pack' encapsulation and (c) $\frac{1}{4}$in. square case encapsulation by Mullard.

Owing to the small dimensions of the chip, a very high standard of precision is demanded in processing the connections from the chip to the leadout wires or soldering tags—gold wire is commonly used for the inter-connections and the leadouts. When all the connections have been completed, the chip is hermetically sealed within its encapsulation in a dry nitrogen atmosphere.

Thin Film ICs

It is possible by the thick and thin film techniques to integrate active components (transistors and diodes, for instance) with passive ones. Current practice involves the addition of the active components to the passive components, the circuit made of film forming what is called a 'hybrid circuit'. It is also sometimes necessary to develop the circuit as a whole by the addition of separate passive elements, for although components like capacitors and inductors can be made in film, the values and Q-factors of these may be too limited for the design in hand.

Basically, therefore, the circuit and some of the components are deposited upon an insulated substrate as films in various patterns of strips and rectangles; in other words, such a circuit is rather like a miniaturised printed circuit—made in a different way—contain-

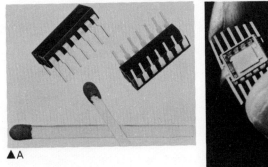

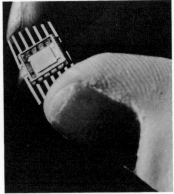

▲A

Fig. 6.7 Various encapsula-   C ▶
tions. See text.

▼B

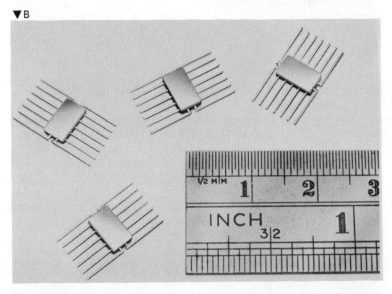

ing not only the wiring but also some of the passive and active elements. It seems that the thin-film technique will eventually develop more towards the total integration of the active elements, making this type of circuit as versatile as the monolithic IC.

Generally, however, the active elements are adapted to the film techniques; they are thus small and not too difficult to mount in the flat circuit. Transistors can be of the conventional type, but an alternative arrangement takes the form of transistors mounted on small ceramic wafers, with pre-tinned contacts.

The trend, however, is towards the direct fitting of the silicon chips into which the transistors are designed (see, for instance, the section under Monolithic ICs). These chips, measuring about 0·6 by 0·6mm, are pre-coated with a very thin layer of glass, while the contacts consist of minute tinned beads mounted in small holes in the film.

Substrates

The substrate upon which the films—representing the circuit conductors, resistors, capacitors and inductors—are deposited is generally high-grade glass or glass-coated ceramic. The material must possess an extremely smooth surface to accommodate the deposited films, which (thin film) are only 10nm. thick!.

The substrates—which are small plates or wafers to facilitate the various processes involving masking and photography, and to allow a number of wafers to be stacked with edge interconnection in a complex assembly—must also be good electrical insulators, of course, have a high electrical quality and good thermal conductivity.

Thin films are applied by the evaporation of metal or carbon on to the substrate in a vacuum, while dielectrics for capacitors are formed by the evaporation of silicon monoxide, resulting in a film of silicon oxide. Thick films are printed and fired.

The master drawings are produced in a similar manner to those for monolithic ICs and, indeed, for ordinary printed circuits, while a common method for generating the pattern on the substrate is akin to that used in printed circuit making. Firstly, a film of metal is evaporated on to the whole surface area of the substrate; it is then coated with a photoresist to the pattern of the master diagram (reduced by photography); and finally, the unwanted areas of metal are etched away.

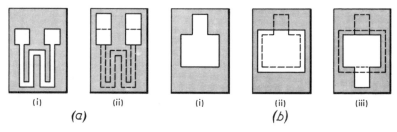

(i)	(ii)	(i)	(ii)	(iii)

(a)　　　　　　　　　　*(b)*

Fig. 6.8　(a) showing the method of generating a thin-film resistor. (i) shows the mask for the resistive film and (ii) the mask for the conductive layer. (b) showing the method of generating a thin-film capacitor. (i) shows the mask for the first electrode, (ii) the mask for the cross-connections and (iii) the mask for the second conductor.

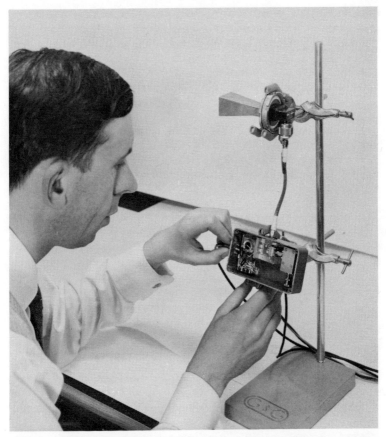

Fig. 6.9   This X-band microwave receiver contains an IC of special type. See text.

The initial film might well be copper, since this is easily removed by etching to form the circuit pattern. After this process, the desired material is then evaporated on to the pattern and the copper is finally removed by etching, thereby leaving the circuit only in the required materials. Other methods have recently been evolved.

Evaporation (Thin Films)

Evaporating the thin films on to the substrates involves placing them on a cylinder frame which is designed to rotate in a vacuum, such as provided by a suitably-sized bell-jar. The cylinder also carries strips or wires of the metal or material which is to form the film, and these are heated by electricity to a temperature just below melting point. There are other methods of evaporation.

To ensure adequate bonding of thin films to the substrates, the substrates themselves are preheated to a temperature of about 300deg.C prior to evaporation. The speed at which the cylinder revolves and the rate of evaporation govern the time taken for a film of specific thickness to form on the substrates, while also determining its degree of uniformity.

Facilities are provided for the continuous monitoring of the resistivity of, at least, one of the substrates during evaporation as a means of determining the film thickness. Because the resistivity of the films tends to rise with time, the circuits are artificially aged by heating in air, which stabilises them.

Resistor elements are made by the evaporation of a nickel-chromium alloy, while conductors are either made by the evaporation of gold or by the depositing of a nickel source on to the films. So-called 'selective tinning' is also adopted to give the various shades of conductivity over the circuit and its elements, for the basic conductivity of nickel, which is not very high, is enhanced by tinning. Resistors are made in the form of zig-zag patterns, as shown in Fig. 6.8(a), while (b) shows the formation of a capacitor.

It has already been mentioned that dielectric films can be produced by the evaporation of silicon monoxide, and the idea is to achieve the greatest capacitance per unit area while ensuring an adequate working voltage, a low dielectric loss and a reasonable temperature coefficient for the nature of the circuit. It is possible to secure capacitances up to $200pF/mm^2$.

When the circuit has been completely fabricated and the separate components have been fitted it is protected against atmospheric effects by hermetic encapsulation into a case carrying connector pins suitable for wiring into an ordinary printed circuit board.

Thick Films

While thin films are vacuum deposited, thick films are printed and fired. The printing constitutes the laying of the circuit conductors and elements on to the substrate, and one approach is screen printing, while the inks are developed to suit the requirements of the conductors and elements. A resistive ink, for example, comprises a mix of palladium monoxide, silver and glass binder. The ink is deposited on to the substrate by means of a squeegee, and the final film characteristic is achieved, after drying, by a firing process, which results in the glass component of the ink fusing to the substrate and hence the formation of the thick film component or circuit.

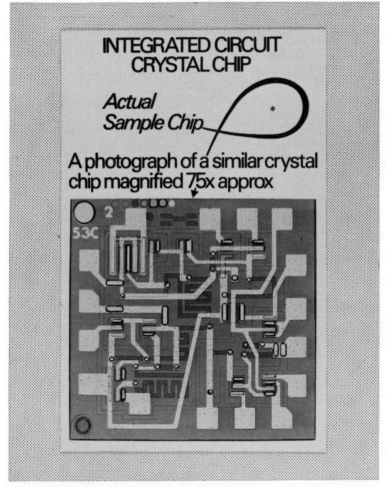

INTEGRATED CIRCUIT CRYSTAL CHIP

Actual Sample Chip

A photograph of a similar crystal chip magnified 75x approx

Fig. 6.10 The IC chip upon which the circuit in Fig. 6.11 is based. The magnified chip, showing the circuit, is reproduced below.

Applications of ICs

A scientific application of integrated circuitry is shown in Fig. 6.9. Here is seen a scientist connecting the output lead to the first stages of an experimental X-band microwave receiver. The box contains an r.f. front-end with a Schottky diode balanced mixer driven by a Gunn effect oscillator. These sections are integrated on two separate substrates, but it is possible for the devices, with the associated circuitry,

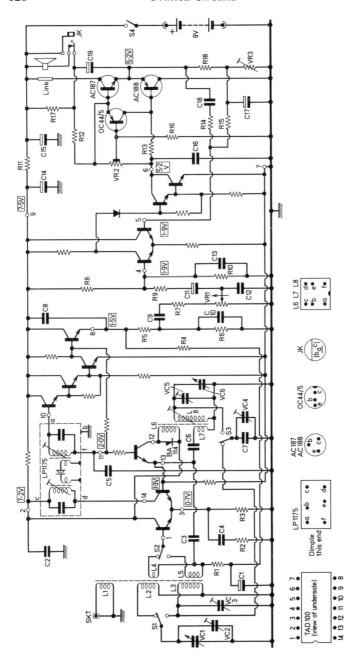

Fig. 6.11   Circuit diagram of the Roberts portable set, Model RIC. 1, based on a Mullard IC. This is fully explained in the text.

to be integrated on a single substrate measuring only 0·6 by 0·9in. (15·2 × 22·8mm).

A more down to earth application is shown in the circuit of the Model RIC.1 portable radio set by Roberts Radio Ltd. in Fig. 6.11. This was the first British solidstate a.m. LW/MW portable to embody a monolithic IC, which is a Mullard Type TAD100 (silicon). The IC caters for all the stages in the set with the exception of the final a.f. amplifier and the push-pull output stage, which use three separate transistors—an OC44/45 and complementary output transistors AC187 and AC188. There is also a separate diode which is used for amplitude limiting of the local oscillator signal.

Another interesting feature of this set is the incorporation of a ceramic resonator (e.g. transfilter) for the control of the i.f. selectivity. The circuit reveals the transistor and resistor elements—eleven of each—contained in the IC.

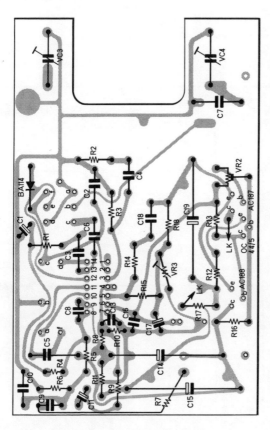

Fig. 6.12 The printed circuit of the Roberts receiver, showing the various points of connection to the IC and discrete components.

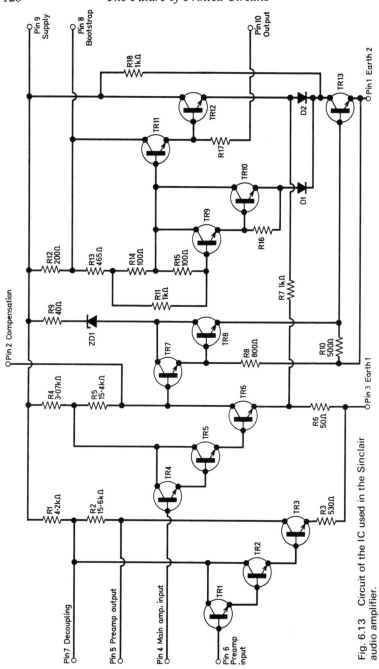

Fig. 6.13   Circuit of the IC used in the Sinclair audio amplifier.

The actual circuit used in the TAD100 is shown greatly magnified in Fig. 6.10, on the top of which is a photograph of an actual sample chip upon which the IC is based. The IC is of flat encapsulation and is fitted into the main printed circuit board by connecting pins, the locations of which can be picked out from the drawing of the printed circuit of the set (Fig. 6.12).

The integrations so far considered mostly provide so-called linear functions: that is, they are able to amplify, detect, limit, invert, modulate or phase shift analogue signals in all spheres of domestic and commercial communications, taking in both sound and vision—monochrome and colour—and all aspects of audio applications, ranging from simple record players to tape recorders and hi-fi equipment.

This should not be taken to imply, however, that all new equipment of this nature is based exclusively on ICs—not yet, anyway!—for it is still necessary to continue using 'hybrid' designs and designs based on discrete components and ordinary printed circuit boards; but, as already intimated, even in some of the apparently less exacting domestic applications ICs are fast coming into the picture.

We have already seen how a single IC is used in an inexpensive portable radio receiver; there are further examples in other areas of domestic electronics. Indeed, one of the first colour television receivers to adopt a single IC was a model of the Rank/Bush/Murphy range. This handles the colour decoding operations—demodulating the colour subcarrier, matrixing the colour-difference information and integrating the control signals to yield primary colour signals for modulating the beams of the picture tube. This one IC replaces 65 discrete components that would normally occupy an area of some 36 square inches (230sq.cm).

Since that first single IC receiver appeared other models have been launched by the same firm and by other manufacturers, with ICs in sections in addition to the colour decoder. An IC is now commonly used for intercarrier amplification and limiting; and some ICs also provide sections for f.m. detection in conjunction with an external coil and one or two discrete components.

ICs are also appearing in hi-fi amplifiers. There is a monolithic IC which combines the preamplifiers and power amplifier of an audio channel. This, complete with heat sink, is not much larger than a 10p piece. The silicon chip is 0·05in. (1·27mm) square by 0·01in. (0·25mm) thick and contains thirteen transistors (two of which are power devices) three diodes and eighteen resistors (Fig. 6.13). R.m.s. power output is 5W, with less than 1% distortion. Frequency response is 5Hz to 100kHz within 1dB.

To get the IC working as a fully-fledged amplifier it must be tied to a relatively simple circuit of discrete components, possibly on an ordinary printed circuit board, to provide the controls of tone and volume; it must also, of course, be connected to a mains or battery power pack.

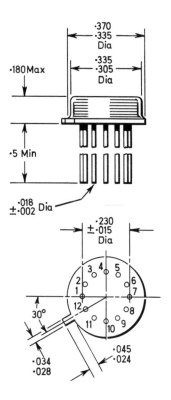

Fig. 6.14 (left) IC encapsulation to TO-5, showing wire leadouts and their numbering.

Fig. 6.15 (below) "Block" diagram of the RCA CA3020 multi-purpose audio monolithic IC.

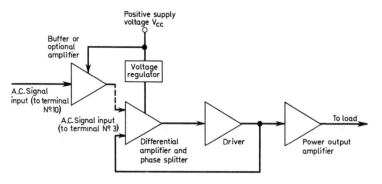

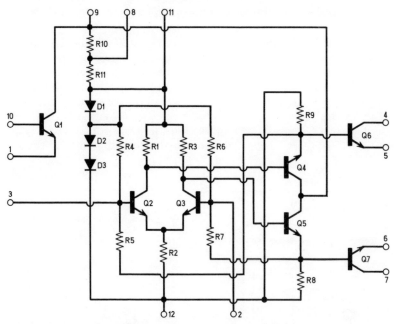

Fig. 6.16   Complete circuit of the CA3020.

Multi-purpose IC

Now let us look at a multi-purpose IC, Type CA3020 by RCA. As this is designed essentially to work as an amplifier—as distinct from a switching device—it is thus of the linear family. It will provide the complete audio channel of a portable radio set, for example, *including* the output stages capable of delivering some 550mW of audio power at a current of 22mA.

The device is encapsulated to TO-5 with twelve leadout wires, as shown in Fig. 6.14, and it is arranged to perform five prime functions, which are: (i) voltage regulator, (ii) buffer or optional amplifier, (iii) differential amplifier and phase-splitter, (iv) driver and (v) power output amplifier, as shown in Fig. 6.15.

A diagram of the circuit is given in Fig. 6.16, the operation of which is as follows. The voltage regulator consists of diodes D1, D2 and D3 with resistors R10 and R11. The diodes are constructed from transistor emitter-base junctions to facilitate temperature tracking from −55deg.C to +125deg.C, and the regulator delivers two potentials to the differential amplifier—a base-emitter supply to point 2 of about 1·4 volts and a base-emitter supply to point 3 of about 2·1 volts.

The differential amplifier/phase-splitter circuit is composed of transistors Q2 and Q3, collector resistors R1 and R3 and biasing resistors R4, R5, R6 and R7. The a.c. signal input may be fed in either to point 10—via the buffer amplifier transistor Q1—or to point 3, using RC-coupling in both cases, and whichever input is adopted the signal is amplified and the 180deg. phase-shift necessary for push-pull drive is achieved between the collectors of transistors Q2 and Q3.

The signal arrives at the emitter-follower transistors Q4 and Q5, forming the driver stage, and feedback resistors R5 and R7 provide

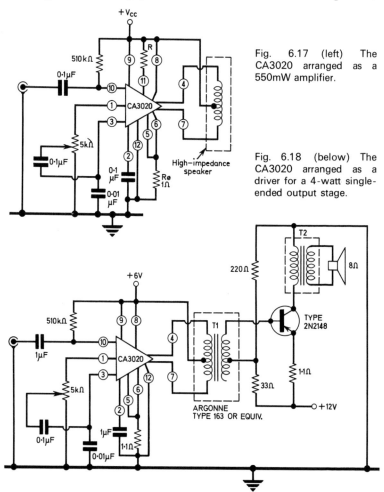

Fig. 6.17 (left) The CA3020 arranged as a 550mW amplifier.

Fig. 6.18 (below) The CA3020 arranged as a driver for a 4-watt single-ended output stage.

d.c. and a.c. stability in the differential amplifier. If these resistors were not used, slight changes in base-emitter potential, transistor gain (beta) and/or resistor value ratios could cause the d.c. voltage between the collectors of Q2 and Q3 to vary from zero. In the circuit, however, application of the emitter-follower voltages from Q4 and Q5 to the differential amplifier through R5 and R7 compensates for any unbalance tendencies.

The power output transistors Q6 and Q7 receive the signal from the emitters of Q4 and Q5 and deliver power to the load in conventional class B push-pull mode. The CA3020 will work with any supply voltage between $+3$ and $+9$ volts, but at supply voltages above $+6$ volts a heat sink is necessary to achieve the maximum power capability.

Fig. 6.20 (right). The CA3020 arranged as a d.c. amplifier.

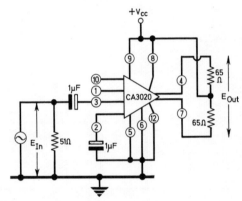

Fig. 6.19. (below) The CA3020 arranged as a driver for a 7-watt Class B push-pull amplifier.

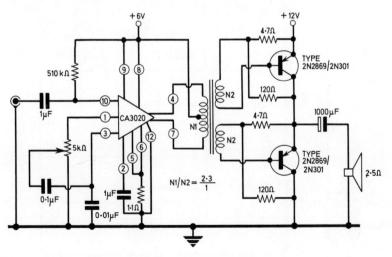

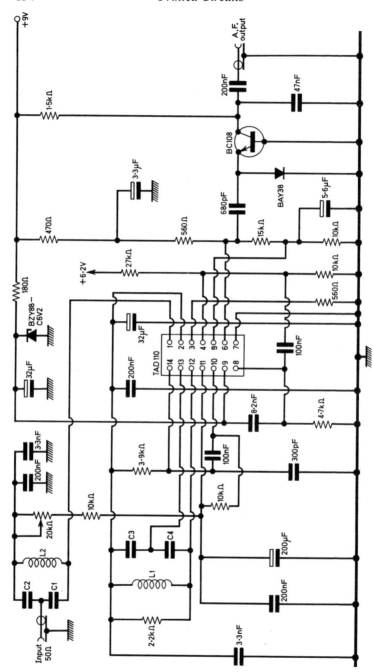

Fig. 6.21 30MHz i.f. strip designed by Mullard round that company's TAD110 silicon monolithic linear IC.

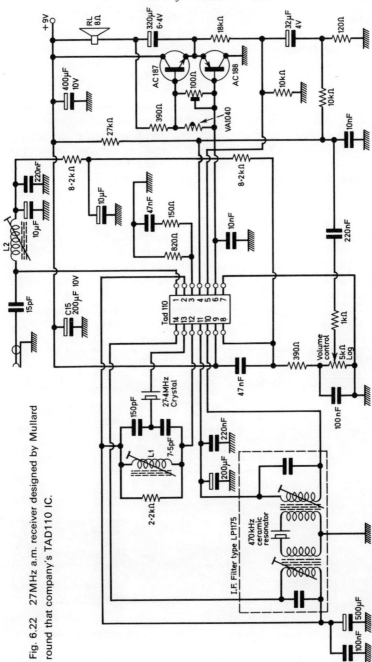

Fig. 6.22 27MHz a.m. receiver designed by Mullard round that company's TAD110 IC.

Fig. 6.17 shows one way in which the IC may be wired to discrete components on a printed circuit board, for instance. Here the input signal is applied to point 10, via an RC network comprising an 0·1μF capacitor and 510kΩ resistor, while a 5kΩ volume control is connected between points 1 and 3, via an 0·1μF capacitor. Other discrete components are also used as the diagram reveals, and the design is for driving a high impedance loudspeaker. A low impedance speaker can be used, however, by interposing a suitable transformer between points 4 and 7 (the primary) and the speaker itself (secondary).

It is also possible to adopt the IC purely as a driver for a higher power amplifier, as shown in Figs. 6.18 and 6.19, the former yielding 4 watts and the latter 7 watts, using suitable output transistors the latter in class B push-pull. The IC arranged as a d.c. amplifier is given in Fig. 6.20.

It will be seen in all of these circuits that the IC is represented by a triangle or arrow head pointing in the direction of signal travel. This is one recognised way (another is by a rectangle) of symbolising the IC, with the connecting points (represented by the leadout wires or tags, depending on the type of encapsulation used) numbered in circles round it.

Two interesting circuits based on the Mullard TAD110 monolithic linear IC are given in Figs. 6.21 and 6.22. The first is a 30MHz i.f.

Fig. 6.23   This photo shows a row of three, four-transistor ICs used in the Scott tuner-amplifier, Model 342-B.

strip and the second a 27MHz a.m. receiver. The TAD110 provides three stages; the first a long-tailed-pair of transistors which may be employed as an amplifier or mixer with d.c.-coupling to the emitter of the local oscillator; the second, used for tuned input or wideband amplification, consists of a Darlington circuit followed by a common-emitter amplifier and an emitter-follower output stage; and the third is basically an amplifier, which can either be used to provide amplification at the same frequency as the second stage or as an audio preamplifier.

The circuit shown in Fig. 6.21, of course, needs a front-end to operate it and also an audio amplifier/output stage, while that in Fig. 6.22 is complete, with audio stages and loudspeaker.

Linear ICs (operational amplifiers) are also to be found in hi-fi tuners and tuner-amplifiers, and a row of four ICs in the i.f. strip of the Scott 342-B tuner-amplifier are pictured in Fig. 6.23. Each of these contains four transistors with associated resistors, and they are tuned by external (i.e. discrete) i.f. transformers. The f.m. front-end of this American model features a field effect transistor (FET), and the combination of this and the ICs provides extremely high sensitivity coupled with low-noise operation, giving a specification of about −40dB quieting from an aerial input signal as low as 2μV.

Switching

So far we have considered ICs acting essentially as linear devices. However, in computers they serve as switching devices, giving the necessary counts, pulses and so forth demanded by computer electronics. It is totally impossible to explore this very specialised aspect of the IC, for this is a science in itself.

It is noteworthy, however, that ICs were aimed initially at satisfying the demands of the computer industry for digital circuits, and from these extended efforts have evolved the more down to earth, linear device upon which this chapter has concentrated. This is because the processing techniques and equipment developed for computers have also been found suitable for linear IC production.

Readers delving into the computer side of electronics will immediately come up against ICs of a specialised kind, so there is very little point but merely to acknowledge them here.

INDEX

Index